A JOURNEY WITHOUT MAPS

DNA,
Diplomacy,
Teaching,
Culture

ROBERT YUAN

A Journey Without Maps

Published by Winter Island Press
Salem, Massachusetts
winterislandpress.com

ISBN: 979-8-9878655-0-7
eBook ISBN: 979-8-9878655-1-4

Printed in the United States of America

Cover design by Yuan Lin

This book is dedicated to my parents,
Tao Feng Yuan
and
Rose Ouang

CONTENTS

A CHINESE FAMILY
From China to the West
1906-2003

My parents were born into a society in search of itself. In the tumultuous years that marked the end of Imperial China, as the nation was rocked by agitation, uprisings, and revolution, my parents became Westernized by choice, hoping that the West would provide a model for a modern China. My most vivid images of them are from when they were in their 30s living in Cuba, but world geography framed their lives: Shanghai, Nanjing, Moscow, Paris, Vichy, Havana, New York, Walnut Creek. My mother, Rose, was talented, beautiful, charming, and sociable. My father, Tao-Feng Yuan or T.F., was serious, organized, professional–an honest man in a world where corruption was ubiquitous. Their trajectory included academic achievement, a brilliant diplomatic career, an unexpected love match, years of war and revolution around the world, and unexpected middle and final chapters in America.

Chinese culture teaches the values of stability, honesty, family. If you live a righteous life, success and happiness should follow. But what if the world you know disappears in the blink of an eye? How do you cope, how do you reinvent yourself in order to survive? Father tried to teach me these lessons and to provide some sense of rationality in an irrational world. Mother gave us, my sister and me, warmth and love, but at the same time insisted on self-reliance, endurance, and education to enable us to make our own way in the world. Both of them were captivating storytellers, and they loved to share tales of their experiences and of the history of our families and our people.

Fate led them to work and live in such diverse societies as France, Cuba, and the United States. In the process they lost their native China, their families, and my father's career. In one lifetime, they were among the elites of the diplomatic corps, exiles, and practically penniless immigrants. But throughout it all, they never forgot China and their heritage. And they hoped that values and visions from that past world would find root in my sister and myself.

Their story began in two different Chinas at the start of the 20th century.

Tao-Feng: From Rural Fukien to Paris and Beyond

My father was born on Nov. 24, 1906, one of seven children in rural Shangshang, in the province of Fukien. His father was a prosperous landlord with an interest in scholarly activities. T.F. was a dedicated student who did his studies through high school in a rural school. Unusual for a student from the countryside, he went on to Amoy and Shanghai to pursue a higher education. Dissatisfied with what was available, he decided to go to France for his university studies. I was told as a child that his father and the village supported his trip to France.

He first went to the Lycee Lakanal, a well-known secondary school in the outskirts of Paris, to become fluent in French and take the required college preparatory courses. He gained admission to the Sorbonne where he majored in modern history and continued his graduate studies at the Ecole de Sciences Politiques with a specialization in diplomacy.

While my father was in Paris, the Communists confiscated the family properties in Fukien and his father asked him to return home. Unwilling to return without his degree, he made a bold effort to complete his academic work in a year and a half (instead of the regular three years) while working nights at a Chinese restaurant to support himself. This gamble paid off. For all of his life, T.F. was immensely proud of his studies in France and most particularly of his degree in diplomacy. His fluency in the French language was acquired during these early years. In 1931, T.F. returned to Shanghai with a few francs in his pocket, no job prospects and no contacts, but with his degree from the Sorbonne. He struggled to start a career in international affairs. One can hardly imagine what it must have been like to be a young man of 25 in the great metropolis of Shanghai without a mentor, money, or connections. He wrote articles on foreign affairs and taught part time at Fudan University. He began to establish a reputation as someone with experience in Europe and the modern world beyond China's borders.

Eventually, as a returnee from abroad, he was offered a position as an adviser in international affairs to the National Defense Council. He was transferred to the Ministry of Foreign Affairs in Nanjing which, following the collapse of the Imperial government in 1911, had become the capital of the Republic of China.

Rose: Daughter of a Diplomat

My mother, Rose Ouang, was born in Guangzhou on July 20, 1916. She was the second of nine children of Ting-chang Ouang (T.C.) and Clara Chen. Ting-Chang had been educated in Louvain, Belgium. From 1925-1933, he served as Minister Plenipotentiary of the Republic of China in Lisbon. T.C. had taken five (one boy, four girls) of his eight children to his foreign posting. All of them were sent to French schools. While abroad, Rose and her sister Anna studied for two years in Florence at the School of the Santissima Annunziata Poggio Imperiale.

Rose became fluent in Italian and French, and her friendships with the daughters of upper class European families introduced her to a different lifestyle. For her whole life, Mother was to retain pleasant memories of summers spent on the beach at Arcachon (France) and Estoril and Caiscais (Portugal). Sometime in the 1930s, the family returned to Nanjing, China, where T.C. became Chief of Protocol in the Ministry of Foreign Affairs.

Nanjing

It is not clear how T.F. made the acquaintance of the Ouang family, but I heard many times that my grandfather had liked the bright young diplomat with a future ahead of him. Grandfather soon decided that he was an appropriate match for his oldest daughter, Marie Louise, but T.F. had set his mind on Rose, the second daughter. My mother was, however, her father's favorite, and he had higher ambitions for her than a marriage to a young junior diplomat. Rose was only 20 but already had a mind of her own and decided she would marry T.F.

Nanjing marked the beginning of a love affair that would last a lifetime. The wedding of Rose and T.F. was a glamorous social event and a happy moment in their lives. Four days later, the young couple left Nanjing for Moscow where T.F. would take up his first foreign posting. When Tsiang Ting-Fu was appointed to be ambassador to the Soviet Union, he chose T.F. to go with him as his secretary.

Late in life, Father would still reflect with a sense of wonder about how Rose had chosen to marry him and share a life that led the young couple away from China and through some of the great upheavals of the twentieth century. This fortuitous appointment also saved them from being in Nanjing at the time of the Japanese brutal murder of hundreds of thousands of Chinese during the Nanjing Massacre in 1937.

The Young Diplomatic Couple in Europe

T.F. saw Russia as a living model of a society undergoing revolutionary change. The country was well on its way to becoming industrialized, and the military parades in Red Square gave evidence of its military power. This was, however, also the time of the Great Purges when high government officials, party functionaries and generals were tried and summarily executed. T.F. could meet and work with a Soviet official one day and he would disappear the next.

In the summer of 1938, Father went to Berlin where he had the opportunity to observe Hitler's Germany up close. Perhaps more than in the USSR, the dictatorial Third Reich had made rapid progress in becoming a modern advanced industrial power with a powerful army and air force. Once an ally and supporter of the Nationalist government, Berlin had now aligned itself with Japan, withdrawn its military advisers from China, and stopped the shipment of vital military equipment and supplies.

In July, 1938 my parents were transferred to Paris where I was born on October 9, 1938. Even though WWII was looming and the international situation was deteriorating, my parents would always remember Paris with a sense of joy and delight. Both were familiar with the city, its culture and language. And to top it all, this was where they had their firstborn son. In their minds, these were the last moments when the lights shone brightly before the darkness of the Nazi occupation descended on their favorite city. T.F. was soon recalled to the wartime capital of Chungking to serve on the National Defense Council.

Japan and China were at war. In February, 1939, my mother took her newborn son and sailed from Marseilles to Shanghai. Though Japan now occupied Shanghai, her family was living in the safety of the French Concession. The family was ecstatic at the return of Rose with her little baby boy and first grandchild. In addition to the grandfather, there were five eager aunts to play and take care of the baby. And taking the baby for a ride was the sure-fire way to get permission to have the use of the car and the chauffeur to go on excursions to the movies, pastry shops and restaurants. These idyllic moments were the last that she would spend with her beloved father, but three of her sisters would relocate to Canada after the war and she would reconnect with them many years later.

In the spring of 1940, T.F. was appointed to be Consul General in Paris at the recommendation of Wellington Koo, a top Chinese diplomat. After journeying from different parts of China, my parents met in Hong Kong for the long trip back to a very different Paris. The voyage was laborious: first a ship to Bombay, then another to Basra (Iraq), then by train to Geneva. By the time they arrived in Paris, France had been defeated and the city was occupied by the Germans. The German authorities allowed T.F. to take up his position, though by this time the only existing French government was in Vichy in unoccupied France. It is ironic that even though both the international situation and my father's diplomatic career were totally uncertain, my parents were still happy to be back in Paris. It did help that, being part of the diplomatic corps, they were not subject to the strict rationing that had been imposed on all ordinary French citizens. Many years later, Mother still remembered giving her bread and staple rations to servants and friends.

For months, they were stranded in Paris in an anomalous diplomatic situation – Germany was allied with Japan, China was at war with Japan and allied with the US. Both Germany and Japan still had diplomatic relations with the US, and France no longer existed as an independent nation. After a few months, T.F. and his family moved to Vichy, maintaining the fiction that there was still a Chinese representation to the puppet French government there. This situation came to an end in 1941 with the bombing of Pearl Harbor and Germany's declaration of war on the US. At that time, Germany requested the withdrawal of all Chinese missions to the German-occupied countries in Europe. This created a serious administrative crisis with displaced Chinese diplomats that needed to be appointed and relocated to new positions. The family moved from Vichy to Lisbon to await orders from the Foreign Ministry.

T.F. expected to be sent to New York and a possible posting in the US. Much to his surprise, he was ordered to join the staff of the Chinese Legation in Havana, Cuba. Where was Cuba? What would he do there? They learned that Cuba was a former Spanish colony located on a small island in the Caribbean ninety miles from the US. It had an agricultural economy and was well known for its rum, rhumba, and cigars. To them this was a pleasant assignment to enjoy while waiting to see how WWII played out. How could they have ever guessed that the family would spend eighteen years there, only to be displaced by another revolution?

Cuba: An Extended Interlude

For my parents, life in Cuba had three periods: the official (1942-1950), post-official (1950-1953) and private (1953-1960). Island life was comfortable and lively. There was a pleasant apartment in Vedado and food was plentiful. My parents could afford private schools for the children, membership at the yacht club, and an animated social life. Both of them learned English and Spanish.

T.F. started out as a secretary in the Chinese Legation and was promoted to Consul General. He was busy in two different domains: in the 1940s, Cuba had a significant Chinese population numbering around 25,000. Most of them had come to work in the sugar cane fields but then had become small farmers, traders, and shop owners. They often got involved in legal problems related to inheritances, taxes, paternity. One of Father's responsibilities was to try to work with the Cuban authorities to resolve these problems. The Consulate had no responsibility for government-to-government affairs. However, being fluent in both English and Spanish and having a network of contacts in Havana made Father an influential interlocutor with the Cuban authorities, exceeding his official position. Rose was an important partner because of her linguistic and diplomatic skills. Her knowledge of Cantonese (the language of the local Chinese) was valuable, and she often would translate for my father who could speak only in Mandarin.

My parents had a very busy social life, one that was uncommonly diverse, with events in the international community, Cuban community, and last but not least, with the local Chinese population. My father was well beloved by the local Chinese for his work in ensuring that their rights and interests were protected. While the local Chinese community was not particularly wealthy or educated, it showed its gratitude in small ways. In our neighborhood, there was a Chinese greengrocer who would push his cart full of fresh vegetables and fruits, then place it in the underground garage every day. He would make a list of what we needed and deliver it. He kept a tab which my mother paid at the end of the month. That would always be an occasion for argument because Mother was convinced that he was undercharging us. I am sure he believed that this was his obligation.

The most amusing moment was one night during the Christmas season when my parents had gone out to a dinner party, leaving me home with the maid. A Chinese farmer came by bringing Christmas gifts which consisted of a suckling pig and a dozen chickens and guinea hens – all alive. We had him leave them in the kitchen. The maid and I stayed up waiting for the return of my parents. As they walked in the door, I excitedly told them that Mr. Wang had come to wish them a Merry Christmas and had left the animals for our holiday dinner.

"Where are they?" asked my mother.

"They are in the kitchen, Mother," I gushed, "and they are all alive."

She scolded me for not telling the truth and went to the kitchen. But when she turned on the lights, I heard loud animal noises followed by a scream. So much for my not telling the truth!

World War II came to an end in 1945, which coincided with the birth of Rosalind, my kid sister. After such a long time, I now had a sibling, a companion, someone to look after. Our lives would be forever linked, often in contrasting ways, parallel but on very different tracks. In the years that followed, the world would change drastically around all of us, but our family survived intact.

The Loss of a Homeland

The end of World War II did not mean that all would be well. The Chinese Civil War intensified, and the People's Liberation Army made steady progress on the battlefield. By 1949, what was left of the Nationalist government had fled to Taiwan, and the People's Republic of China was declared in Beijing. The Consulate in Havana was closed and Father was ordered to return to Taipei, Taiwan now being the last bastion of the Nationalist government. The world had changed, and the consequences were direct and personal.

At the age of 43, Father's diplomatic career came to an end. A dedicated anti-Communist, Father would not join the new government in Beijing, but he also knew that Taiwan no longer represented the government of China. And it was almost certain that the Communists would occupy Taiwan.

Caught in a political limbo, Father listened to the advice of his Cuban friends which included the Cuban president, Carlos Prio Socarras. They advised him that our family should remain in Cuba. Prio also offered to help him get financial support. With that and the creation of an international consulting practice, Father settled down to a manageable life in Havana. For my parents, this was a shattering experience as they were suddenly cut off from their country, their families, and my father's career. And they were faced with an unknown future on a small island in the Caribbean.

But this post-diplomatic period was not to last very long.

On March 10, 1953, Fulgencio Batista ousted the Prio government in a military coup. For the next seven years, our family struggled economically as my parents tried their luck with various enterprises. T.F. continued to do some consulting, traded in the US stock market (under the tutelage of a wealthy Chinese investor), and dabbled in the import-export business. Mother worked part-time teaching Chinese at a school run by two Catholic Chinese priests.

The years in Cuba after my father left the diplomatic service affected my parents in very different ways. Rose developed a steely resolve to do everything necessary to keep the family afloat, taking up various small jobs and keeping expenses to a minimum. Father was more choosy about what he would do, but neither his background nor his temperament would make him into a successful businessman. Father was able to preserve two extravagant expenses, private school for the children, and membership at the yacht club. In a way, both were essential to his self-image.

While life in Cuba had already been difficult, it would take a turn for the worse. The situation there changed dramatically on July 26, 1953, when a group of insurrectionists led by a young lawyer named Fidel Castro attacked the Moncada army barracks in Santiago de Cuba. The revolt was bloodily crushed, and Castro was arrested, tried, and sentenced to years in jail. However, after being released early as part of a general amnesty, Castro went into exile in Mexico. From there, he and a small group of his followers made a stormy trip on the yacht Granma, landing in the eastern province of Oriente. The return of Castro triggered a hard and bloody struggle between his 26 of July Movement and Batista's army. This conflict was mainly fought by the peasant guerrillas in the mountains of the Sierra Maestra and a growing urban resistance movement, particularly in Havana and Santiago de Cuba. The political and economic instability made my family's day-to-day existence even more precarious.

On New Year's Eve, 1959, Batista fled. A few days later, Fidel and his victorious army of 'barbudos" (bearded ones) entered Havana. No one knew then that this would mark the beginning of a Marxist revolutionary regime and a continuing policy of confrontation with the United States. The Castro government recognized the People's Republic of China, which opened an embassy in Havana and began sending a growing number of advisers to the island. China was intent in promoting an alternative model of Communism to that of the Soviet Union. Such a strategy could be pursued by exporting revolution to Latin America and expanding Chinese influence in the Western Hemisphere. But in order to do so, Beijing would need to develop a cadre with expertise in Latin American affairs. Chinese officials made overtures to my father.

At the same time, I had graduated from high school and moved to the US for university. Uncertain as to his future and that of his family, T.F. fled Havana in the summer of 1960, followed later in the fall by Rose and daughter Rosie.

Starting Over (Again) in the United States

For more than twenty years, while I went to school and built my life, my parents lived in New York, in a high-rise apartment building in Brooklyn. Father found a job as a librarian at the NYU School of Medicine while mother worked in the coffee shop at the Summit Hotel. For both, this was a dramatic descent from the life of prestige and comfort in the diplomatic service. At least in the case of Father, he had a white collar position where he associated with doctors and students. For Mother, it was a much harsher service job with long hours and low pay. But I imagine what may have been hardest of all was going from being the one who is served to the one who is serving. And yet, my mother was able to do this with determination and grace for many long years. She was well respected in her work and became a Union representative in her hotel.

During these New York years, both Rosie and I spent varying periods in Brooklyn. I pursued my studies for a PhD in Molecular Biology at the Albert Einstein College of Medicine and lived with my parents for two years. Rosie did her undergraduate work at Antioch College and then her PhD at Boston University. Her career and marriage took her to Duke University and then on to UC Berkeley. Both of us would regularly visit the Brooklyn apartment, eventually bringing along our spouses and children.

It was through an accident of fate that I met Michael Tsien when both of us were taking a summer workshop in Berkeley in 1960. We briefly shared an apartment in New York while I was doing my graduate studies before Michael moved to Detroit to work at Ford Motors. One consequence of our friendship was that I started dating his sister, Ying-Ying. It was then that the parents discovered that Michael and Ying-Ying were the grandchildren of Wellington Koo, the top Chinese diplomat who had recommended my father so long ago to the Chinese Consulate in Paris. Not only did my parents become good friends of the Tsiens, but Father was able to reconnect with Ambassador Koo and enjoy conversations on current international affairs with his new old friend. He spent many happy hours doing research on China's diplomatic history and wrote several articles on diplomacy and international affairs for journals in Taiwan. Indeed, in his retirement years, he rediscovered his deep love and interest in international diplomacy and came back to research and writing. We know that these activities gave him deep satisfaction.

My parents had an interesting relationship with the Tsiens. Although outwardly of totally different temperaments, they shared the same loss of country and the experience of re-establishing themselves in the US. Another commonality, which was rarely if ever discussed, was that each of them had been on his own since their teenage years, and so were self-made people. T.F. had traveled to France when not yet 20, perhaps the first from his town. Rose had lived in Europe as a teenager. Pat had left China when she was 15 years old, and K.C. had been on his own ever since his father died when he was 14. Although they were Chinese and had been brought up in Chinese culture, they were all also highly Westernized.

In 1981, my parents retired. My expectation was that they would move down to Maryland and live close to me. It was a surprise when they decided to move to California. Rosie found them a nice townhouse in Walnut Creek. For the first time in their lives, they had their own home. Father had his own study where he could have his books and do his writing. Both enjoyed the small patio, the community pool, and the daily walks in the neighborhood. Walnut Creek was an easy drive from Moraga, so they could see Rosie, Sung-Hou, and the two grandchildren. My father found Walnut Creek idyllic; he was happy to be an American citizen who now had his own version of the American dream. My mother was less satisfied. She liked it well enough, but her memories of Shanghai, Paris, Lisbon, and Havana would always be with her. Walnut Creek was just a bit too provincial.

As the years passed, my mother developed Alzheimer's disease and it was no longer possible for them to live in their townhouse. They moved into an assisted living facility in Moraga, just a few blocks from Rosie's house. This was not a place where they would have wished to live out their last years. But, unusually for elderly Chinese, they had chosen to protect their children from the responsibility of taking care of them. And luckily, they adapted very well to their new living environment.

My father died on April 19, 1999 at the age of 92; my mother passed away on May 1, 2003 at the age of 86. They are both buried on a high hill in a cemetery near Berkeley where many other Chinese are also buried.

A Lasting Influence

Rarely does a day go by that I do not think of my parents. Both had a good sense of humor. I can remember many parties when we were all laughing and enjoying ourselves, even when finances were tight. When I lived in Europe in the 1970s, my parents made a trip to Italy, France, and Switzerland. They took an American Express tour to revisit all the places that they had known so well and of which they had such fond memories. They dressed elegantly, my father always in tie and jacket, my mother always in dresses.

I know I have inherited their wanderlust and enjoyment of the pleasures of life, as well as an interest in political affairs. My parents had the advantage of starting their professional and married lives early, and of living a long time. This may have made it easier to navigate their ways through the global upheavals of their times and to adapt to life in different countries, among people with diverse values. Certainly, their early exposure to Europe helped them throughout their lives.

My parents were so different and yet so similar. Father was what I would call a Neo-Confucian, with strong moral views on the responsibilities of an individual with regards to his family and his society, the importance of scholarship and respect for one's elders. This was melded with the liberal traditions of the France he experienced as a student. Mother was an unusual combination of the romantic, filled with life and adventure, and the hardheaded realist committed to the survival of her family as unimaginably hard times came to pass. She was alive to all the senses, enjoying good food and wine, talking with friends and strangers. She was considered by all to be a charming and generous person. As a young couple, whenever we visited my parents in Brooklyn, my mother would always give Ying a $20 bill to buy something that she liked. In fact, my mother always believed in cash; upon her death, we found wads of $20 bills rolled up in the pockets of various coats.

From my own perspective, the greatest irony of their lives was that although they lived only seventeen years in Cuba, this little island was a dominant theme for the rest of their lives. In many ways they saw themselves as more Cuban than American, even after forty years in the US. Their conversations with us were always interspersed with words in Spanish, and both adopted the terms Mami and Papi when they became grandparents. They loved the island and its people, particularly the inherent generosity and joy of life. Even years later, Mother would talk about the foods, the fruits, and the music while Father reminisced about the loyal friends he had made.

From a distance, I can see all that they lost over those many years. Yet somehow, they never became bitter or angry, or at least did not show their disappointments to their family. My memories of my parents are of their fondness for their lives before and for what they still had, their delight in the successes of their children, and the pleasures of being grandparents.

THE PURSUIT OF EDUCATION
Havana - Yellow Springs - Manhattan
1943-1961

I have said that my parents were different from each other in significant ways. A visual example of the difference in their characters was in their handwriting. Most of T.F.'s writings were in the artistic style of Chinese calligraphy. Rose had been taught by the nuns of the Sacred Heart and her handwriting had the elegance and beauty of a manuscript. Even though she had never had the advantages of a higher education, it did not stop her from encouraging and nurturing the educational aspirations of her children. Thanks to my parents, Rosie and I were the fortunate recipients of the best education available. This inspired a hungry curiosity and relentless pursuit of understanding that would become a central underpinning of my life. Of all the gifts T.F. and Rose bestowed over the years, this may be the one with the most profound and far reaching impact on my life.

Columbus School: The Early Years

My parents enrolled me in the Columbus School in Havana as soon as I was ready for the first grade. They chose this school because La Salle, run by the Salesian Brothers, held all its classes in Spanish, while the international school, the Ruston Academy, taught only in English. At the Columbus School, classes were in both Spanish and English. We took an equal number of courses in each language, and the classes in English were modeled after those in American schools.

The scholastic tradition promoted a fierce competition based on academic excellence. The most tangible sign of this was the academic medal. In primary school, the medals were made of bronze and had the shape of a small shield. In the center was the school symbol, surrounded by the inscription "Por Excelencia" (for Excellence), the grade and the year. In high school, the medals were silver disks with the emblem in the middle, a simpler and more elegant design.

For primary school students, academic averages were calculated each week and the individual with the highest score would get the medal for the week. If someone else had a higher score the following week, possession of the medal would pass on to him/her. At the end of the academic year, the overall winners would get to keep the medals. Most importantly, the medals were awarded at a public assembly at noon on Fridays. Each medal winner would be announced, and if a medal had to change hands, the former recipient would have to pin the medal on his/her successor. Winning and losing took place in front of the assembled teachers and students. Most often I got to keep the medal.

High School

In high school, the Spanish curriculum followed the strict requirements set by the Cuban government while the smaller number of English courses focused on language training and culture. Twice a year, we were required to take official exams similar to the French baccalaureate. We had to pass all of them in order to receive an official high school degree.

High school was much more challenging to me than junior high or primary school. I met my nemesis in the form of a Puerto Rican boy named Ernesto Beauchamp. He prided himself on being an American (though the Cuban boys did not consider him a real American) and therefore better in the English classes. I did not find Beauchamp very "simpatico" (likable), but he was academically good and a fierce competitor. For the first time, I had to develop a strategy to keep the medal, which changed hands in high school only every month.

I could be certain that Beauchamp would put every effort into getting high scores on the exams and major lab projects. It was also certain that our differences in those major assignents would be small. Winning or keeping the medal meant deliberate attention to detail and picking up points in all the small tasks (a quiz here, a presentation there, a notebook report). If I could manage a small edge or a minimal loss on the exams, the cumulative effect from the small assignments added up and ensured a margin for victory. The climax came in the third year when possession of the medal swung back and forth between us. I was confident that I could edge out Beauchamp in the end. At the end of the year, I was declared the winner, because he had been late to class a few times. The awarding of the medals taught me that success was less about working harder and more about working smarter.

For many, the adolescent high school years are filled with uncertainty and anxiety. I was no exception. Most of the boys at the Columbus School spent their time and energy on three things: sports, dancing, and girls. These were certainly not activities that I was very good at. I excelled academically both in English and Spanish. I found my sanctuary at a large library of the Cuban-American Foundation, which had an extensive collection of English language books. I also enjoyed the small but luxurious library at the yacht club. My father encouraged us to spend more time at the club for sports and social activities, but I would disappear into the library for hours at a time.

In 1956, while my head was buried in books and studies, Fidel Castro and a group of followers landed in Oriente Province. They made their way into the rugged mountains of the Sierra Maestra where they aggressively recruited the local peasants. The Sierra Maestra became the center of resistance to the Batista dictatorship. Even in our private school, students would whisper about the activities of the fidelistas. There were always rumors as to whether someone's cousin or close friend had made his way to the Sierra Maestra and joined the guerrilleros. Demonstrations periodically shut down the University of Habana. This raised the question of what would happen to us once we graduated from high school. Would the universities even be open when we were ready to continue our studies?

Preparing for College

Despite the unrest, education remained the principal goal of my parents as it is in all Chinese families. Rose and T.F. had a somewhat different outlook molded by their own experience, but each was committed to my getting a solid and useful education. Both parents believed that it was important that I become skilled in a discipline where I could earn a living regardless of where I ended up. They had seen enough brilliant diplomats, lawyers, and political scientists forced out of their native lands, unable to continue their careers in their new countries. For them, as for many Chinese parents, this meant that their son would have to go into a scientific or technical field. As a high school senior, my preference was to study medicine, but it was not certain that a physician could easily work in a country of his choice. We decided I should try engineering and see how that worked out.

My parents were also convinced that the best solution would be for me to go to university in the United States, so choosing one was our first dilemma. I made plans to start college in the US in the fall of 1955. How to finance this was another dilemma. T.F. had a good friend who not only was familiar with the US educational system, but whose son Richard had applied to US universities the year before. Richard had ended up at Johns Hopkins University. I inherited a large pile of university catalogs from Richard and began the laborious task of understanding the American system of higher education. This process resulted in my being accepted to three schools: Yale University, an Ivy League bastion in New Haven, Connecticut; Stevens Institute of Technology, an engineering school in Hoboken, New Jersey; and Antioch, a progressive liberal arts college in Yellow Springs, Ohio. These three institutions could not have been more different. Neither I nor my parents had any basis for choosing one over the others.

At this point fate stepped in. An Antioch alumnus who had settled in Havana contacted me for an interview. Brandon Robinson was a bright and engaging man who did a fine job of describing the uniqueness of Antioch College. Characteristics such as small classes, the honor system, the cooperative program (with alternating periods on and off-campus on jobs), and a community government (where students shared in the governance of the school) were novel and attractive. My parents and I saw that the earnings from the coop jobs would allow me to pay for part of my college education. So it was that I made one of the most fateful decisions in my life. I chose Antioch College.

Leaving Cuba

Many of us remember our mothers as women of a certain age who fussed over us and reminisced about our childhood achievements and foibles. My last summer in Havana created very different memories of my mother. Those summer nights were balmy and enchanting. Long after my father and sister had gone to bed, my mother and I would sit on our balcony listening to LP's of Viennese waltzes, Italian operas, Cuban boleros and cha-cha-chas, and Broadway shows. We talked the nights away. Or perhaps it is more accurate to say that she talked and I listened. Much of it was about her school days in Italy, the social flurry of republican Nanjing, and the glory of Paris before the war. We talked in Spanish and English with some Chinese thrown in. They were very cosmopolitan conversations.

I felt that she thought this was our last chance to spend this kind of time together before I would be gone to a foreign land and lost to her. The underlying message was that whatever I achieved would depend on hard work, smarts, and confidence. Equally important, I should always seize the opportunity to enjoy life to its fullest. These delightful nights created a memory of my mother as someone magically young, very beautiful, charming and witty, and quintessentially sure of herself.

As the last summer weeks drifted by, Rose insisted against my obstinate resistance that I learn how to cook. During one fierce argument, she said, "The only way you will be certain that you can eat your favorite dishes is by learning how to make them yourself."

"Hah," I riposted, "I will leave that to my wife or girlfriend."

She shook her head. "You know, young girls no longer know how to cook, much less cook your favorite dishes." Then she clinched it: "If you are a good cook, girls will always accept your invitation to dinner. Full and happy after a delicious and comfortable meal, they are likely to curl up and stay the night."

Being ignorant of matters relating to young ladies, I chose to take her advice. With seriousness, I learned to steam rice, do stir fries, grill pork ribs, make sweet and sour pork, braise fish, and even branch out into French dishes such as coq au vin and boeuf bourguignon. Mother was right, the art of cooking, whether expressed in a simple grillade over a campfire or a multiple course dinner, was invaluable in making and keeping friends including those of the opposite sex.

I left Cuba for Ohio in August 1955, thinking only of college and new friends and possibilities. No one had any idea that in a short time, my family would also come to the United States, not as students or diplomats, but as refugees.

Antioch College: More Than Books

I was a very young sixteen when I left for college in the US It was a long trip to Ohio in the heartland of America, worlds away culturally as well as geographically. All on my own in this new world, I planned on earning an engineering degree and returning home to Cuba. But plans change. Cuba was in the midst of a revolution and no one could predict its final outcome. Four years later, my family was forced to leave Cuba and move to New York.

In August of 1955, the week before the launch of my new life in Ohio, I flew to New York to spend a few days with my Aunt Anna. Her husband, T.Y. Lee, was the general manager of the Bank of China in New York. He was charged with getting me outfitted for college and instructing me on the intricacies of American college life. However, Uncle T.Y.'s knowledge of US higher education was limited to the Ivy League and had little relevance to the bohemian and anti-establishment ways of Antioch College. Uncle T.Y. took me to Rogers Peet, a store that specialized in clothes for young college men. There I was duly decked out with grey wool flannel trousers, a tweed sports jacket, button-down oxford shirts, ties, and loafers. As it turned out, this wardrobe did not fit the casual environment of Antioch.

From New York I took a long overnight train ride to Xenia, Ohio, where I and other freshmen were picked up by college representatives. The short ride to Yellow Springs took us through flat green fields. Yellow Springs was the smallest village I had ever been in with a population of 2,000 (exclusive of college faculty and students).

Freshman week was arduous and draining particularly for a foreign student. First, there were days of multiple-choice tests, which I was totally unfamiliar with. I did not understand that the objective was to establish the courses that I needed to take. If my scores were high enough, I could skip the lower level courses and start with higher level courses. This would give me the freedom to take elective courses later on. Then, in order to balance the long hours of academic and psychological testing, we were required to participate in a freshman project. This involved dismantling a series of barracks that had been used as temporary dormitories and transporting the materials to a site in Glen Helen (a thousand-acre natural preserve that belonged to the college) where we were to build a school camp. Since I had never been involved in either physical labor or construction, this was a totally novel experience. My classmates seemed to enjoy the experience, while I found it rather curious to find girls climbing on roofs and hammering away at boards. As for myself, testing and labor made for very long and tiring days.

My first year was fulltime on campus, and adapting to a totally new academic and social system required all my energy. While the work was not particularly difficult, I was required to take a variety of courses that fell into three categories: general education, general science, and courses in my science major, which seemed to be shifting. I had already begun to move away from engineering and into chemistry. The connection between these three types of courses was not at all obvious to me, and I had to expand my English vocabulary for all my classes.

I was lucky to get a half-time job working for the Wright Patterson Anthropometric Project. Air Force flight crews were carefully measured so that they could have customized flight gear. The project specialists had decided that it was as efficient and far cheaper to take multiple photographs of each flyer and have students take the measurements on the photos. There were many hundreds of photographs, and about 130 individual measurements had to be made on each one. I found out that I could do without the technical equipment and use calipers and metal rulers and, by organizing the process, could speed up the data acquisition. I got a lot of satisfaction out of solving problems and making the systems more efficient.

I found college social life a total mystery. On the weekends, most of the other students in my residence hall used to go for beers at one of the two bars in the village. Being sixteen, I was not old enough to drink alcoholic beverages. As Thursday and Friday came around and the fellows were trying to get dates for the weekend, the level of anxiety escalated. I did not know any girls and had no idea how one went about asking a girl out or, for that matter, knowing what to do if she accepted the invitation.

As the quarter progressed, I came under increasing pressure from my hallmates to go on a date. Several of them encouraged me to go on a blind date (a totally mysterious concept to me). Finally, one evening, the designated matchmaker phoned the designated girl and handed the phone over to me. I understood that I was supposed to introduce myself and then ask her to go to the movies. But I was tongue tied and less than coherent in introducing myself.

All of a sudden, she stopped me and said brightly, "You have an accent!"

I agreed that I had an accent (after all I was a foreign student), but before I could go any further, she said, "Ohh, this is exciting, let me try and guess where you are from. Just keep talking and I will try to identify your accent."

In the meantime, my hallmates were crowding around trying to figure out what was happening. Thoroughly embarrassed, I kept talking until she interrupted.

"Stop, stop," she commanded. "I've got it. I know where you are from."

I caught my breath and blurted out, "Where??"

"Schenectady," she asserted with triumph.

I had no idea what she was talking about. "What is Schenectady?" I had lost all interest in going out with this person who seemed to be keen on Schenectady and its inhabitants. The date never happened.

The Co-op Experience

The academic year was organized into alternative periods of study and a work program called co-op. Courses were designed to last for twelve weeks, to be continued when the student returned to campus. The college was responsible for the co-op placements, and credits and grades were given for the co-op periods. At the end of the study quarter, each student would examine the posted jobs and fill out an application for up to five of them. Depending on experience and seniority, he/she might get the position for which he/she had applied or end up with something totally unexpected. I always felt an odd combination of fear and excitement when I checked the job assignments posted outside the Personnel Department.

Going on co-op was a true adventure. The practical questions were: What? Where? How? The what had to do with the nature of the job you would be doing and its relationship to your major and your career plans. The where meant that the assignment could be anywhere in the US, and I would have to find my way there and arrange for affordable housing. Since, even in those days, cheap and acceptable living quarters were hard to come by, this meant that I had to find other Antiochians with whom to share digs. These roommates might be close friends or total strangers. How required integrating the job experience, living in a novel community, and continuing some course work.

For my first co-op, I had hoped to get a research position at a major eastern city. Instead, I did not get any further than Xenia, Ohio, only nine miles from Yellow Springs. Dicks Armstrong Pontius Company (DAP), a major manufacturer of putty and glazing compounds, needed an assistant in their research lab. I was responsible for making and testing new formulations for their products. The tests examined the physical and chemical properties of the new formulas, and if they met certain minimum standards, they would be applied to wall or window surfaces for field tests. This lab work took only some of my time; for the rest I helped on the production line (e.g., moving raw materials, cleaning up, setting up tests).

Making putty was a source of great amusement to my friends. But even though I did not get to do much chemistry and felt stuck at DAP for two quarters, I learned a lesson in real life. While for me this was just a temporary co-op job, for my fellow workers (who were not unionized) this minimum-wage work was what they'd be doing for life.

Seniority allowed for better choices. My next co-op got me further, both scientifically and geographically. I went to the research lab of F.C. Huyck and Sons, located in Rensselaer, New York, a suburb of Albany. F.C. Huyck specialized in the manufacture of papermaking felts. As a lab assistant, I was responsible for various chemical treatments on the wool felts to increase their durability and papermaking characteristics. I not only got to apply my chemistry knowledge, but also found it to be a much more congenial work environment in which many of the staff chemists (some of whom had graduate degrees) were keen on teaching me protein chemistry and encouraging me to try experiments. This was my second co-op experience in industry. For the first time, I noticed that even in a traditional niche with defined products, research and innovation were essential to remaining competitive.

Even though I had an Antioch roommate, I found that my social life gravitated towards the International House where I had the opportunity to meet foreign students from the various colleges and universities in upstate New York.

An American Romance

It was the end of August, 1958, and I had just finished my summer session back in Yellow Springs. There was a one week break before the start of fall classes and the beginning of my fourth year. The campus was empty and silent. Having nowhere to go, I just hung out with my roommate John and Susan, the girlfriend of Harry, one of my good friends.

The summer session had been grueling but the weather that Monday was almost Mediterranean, a nice break from the usual soggy Ohio summer. John had disappeared somewhere when Susan dropped by around 9:30 p.m., so we walked to the Old Trail Tavern in the village to have a couple of beers. The tavern was almost empty, so they closed early. The evening was lovely and it was too early to turn in, so we decided to go for a walk in the glen. Walking in the glen at night was tricky without a flashlight, particularly descending the steep stone steps down to the creek. Fortunately, a full moon helped us to find our way. The trail took us along the creek to the falls and up to a well-known landmark. In a small clearing under a large old oak tree, there was a rock with an inscription from Hugh Taylor Birch, a few lines from one of his daughter's poems.

Rays of moonlight filtered through the forest canopy but not bright enough to be able to read the poem. I borrowed a match and crouched by the rock to read the lines.

> The earth smells old and warm and mellow,
> and all things lie at peace.
> I too serenely lie here under the white-oak tree,
> and know the splendid flight of hours
> All blue and gay, sun-drenched and still.

Apparently, my poetry reading by moonlight was more comedy than drama. What had started as a stifled giggle changed into loud, spontaneous laughter. I never had time to either reflect or comment. I was tackled and toppled from my crouching position, next I felt the light touch of lips on mine, followed by a far more serious kiss. I still recall the curious blend of smells, the pungent smokiness of tobacco with the gentle fragrance of perfume and throughout it all, the embarrassment and chagrin at not being sure of what was happening nor being in charge. Darkness gave way to the soft light of dawn as we eventually made our way back to campus.

That week was filled with magic. We walked, talked, swam at the pool, read, and talked some more. But with the passing of hours, we knew that school would soon start and, with it, Harry's return. Susan insisted that she would take responsibility and let Harry know that she wanted to break their engagement. And so she did. We were all marvelously civilized and very understanding, three good and decent young people fallen into an unintended situation. We remained friends, but we were never the same again.

Susan and I came from different worlds. I was a serious chemistry major looking ahead to graduate school and a research career. Her major would be English or Fine Arts. I was of Chinese origin and from Cuba, and the only America I knew was the America of small-town Ohio. Susan was from Boston and her life was one of private prep schools, houses on Beacon Hill, sailing on the Charles River. And while most of us went around in the bohemian uniform of blue jeans, khakis, denims, and sweatshirts, her preference was for the Ivy League look of wool skirts, crew neck sweaters, blazers and knee socks. And she had the clean scrubbed, handsome look of WASP New England.

The end of summer was the start of a tumultuous and thoroughly exhilarating autumn. I struggled to balance a heavy course load composed mainly of my required chemistry and physics courses with working twenty hours a week at the Air Force lab and being the hall adviser to a group of twenty underclassmen. Managing this would have been a challenge under the best of circumstances, but it was beyond me as I tried to understand what was happening. My focus on the sciences was becoming diluted as Susan introduced me to a new world of novels, plays, poetry and writing. I spent hours and hours devouring Thomas Wolfe, Faulkner, Steinbeck, Eugene O'Neill, Arthur Miller ... and A. A. Milne. Chemistry no longer seemed so compelling. I started to question my carefully constructed career plans.

My relationship with Susan was a source of gossip and amusement for our friends, particularly on a campus where there were probably no more than a dozen Asian students. Her hallmates liked me, encouraged me, and made me into their project for that quarter. At the same time, John (as an Army reservist) and I (as a foreign student) had been charged with advising a special group of students: veterans, foreign students and transfers. Many of them were older and far more experienced than I, and observed my romantic tribulations with detached good humor. But our moments of heightened sensitivity were dampened by the fear that things were spinning beyond our control. Or, as Susan said to me, "Oh, old boy, we are really making a mess of it all."

She talked often of her family, whom she very much wanted me to meet. I found her mother distinguished, intelligent, and soft-spoken. But she did not approve of our relationship, and if Susan did not abide by the family's wishes, they would no longer pay for her college. Our conversations became more intense and imbued with an underlying sadness. And then, just a couple of weeks before Thanksgiving, she told me that she was dropping out of school, and she might enroll at BU for the spring semester. Two days later, she was gone. At a loss, I listened to the advice of John and my friends and started putting back the wreckage of my life.

But, as Bogey said in the film "Casablanca," the problems of two little people hardly matter when your world is coming apart. As I was dallying in the glen, in Cuba, Fidel Castro and his guerrillas had come down from the Sierra Maestra. By November, a fidelista column led by Che Guevara was moving on the central city of Santa Clara. Batista's army moved to defeat Che in a large set piece battle. The great fear was that the final battle would be for Havana itself, leading to the destruction of the city or, alternatively, a government collapse leading to widespread chaos and lawlessness. By New Year's Eve, Batista had fled the island. Fidel entered Havana a few days later. And there I sat in Yellow Springs, Ohio, utterly powerless to do anything for my family.

I felt increasingly at a loss. I was alone amidst the wreckage of my life: missed course work, lost job hours, and advisee time. My home country was falling apart and my family was in danger. My images of Cuba seemed to be fading, but I could not imagine myself living in a place like Yellow Springs or Albany. And while I was making progress with my English, this was mainly associated with schoolwork. When it came to feelings and emotions, I still tended to think in Spanish. Until Susan. Thanks to her, I became acquainted with a whole body of US literature. I became better able to articulate my own experiences and emotions in English. As many other immigrants before me, I was becoming part of the American experience.

I have been back to the rock under the great oak tree many times. Susan left me two books, "Collected Plays" by Eugene O'Neill and "The Complete Winnie the Pooh" by A. A. Milne. Both serve as reminders that life is a series of ups and downs, and that our job is to live it fully.

> Always spring comes again bearing life! Always again! Always, always forever again! – Spring again! – life again! – summer and fall and death and peace again! – but always, always, love and conception and birth and pain again – spring bearing the intolerable chalice of life again! – bearing the glorious blazing crown of life again!
>
> -*The Great God Brown*, Eugene O'Neill

"Pooh, promise you won't forget about me, ever. Not even when I'm a hundred."
Pooh thought for a little.
"How old shall I be then?"
"Ninety-nine."
Pooh nodded.
"I promise," he said.
- *The Complete Winnie the Pooh,* A. A. Milne

Growing Up

As I moved into upper level chemistry courses, I felt more confident about being able to choose my job assignments. My third co-op job was as a lab technician at Diamond Chemicals in Painesville, Ohio, about thirty miles east of Cleveland. I arrived in the middle of a blizzard. This seemed to be the norm in Painesville. With snow up to my thighs, going to work every day was a daunting struggle. Diamond Chemicals was a producer of a particular class of organic compounds (halogenated aromatic rings) which were often used as pesticides. Against the gray wintry skies, the large manufacturing plant with its clouds of noxious fumes was a depressing sight. Fortunately for me, my job was in the research division where we were assigned the task of synthesizing variants of a selected compound. If a new compound was made, we would determine its physical and chemical properties and test it for its possible use as an agrochemical product. I worked for a senior chemist who was very capable, but also a hard taskmaster. The days were long and required a combination of patience and careful attention to detail. Science was becoming ever more real. It was at that time that I got my first patent for the synthesis of a new compound, a matter of great excitement.

As the Antioch years were drawing to an end, I tried to take measure of what I had accomplished so far. The alternating periods of work and study had provided a unique perspective. Just as I was getting tired of classes, exams and labs, I would move on to a co-op job in a strange new city. When the work routine was becoming tedious and intellectually unchallenging, it was time to return to the world of books and ideas. In practice, I found that while I liked organic chemistry and was good at it, I was much less certain that I wanted to do that for the rest of my life. The liberalism of our academic program had sharply affected my curriculum. Waiving a large number of introductory courses enabled me to select upper level electives. I had indulged my curiosity: instead of taking more chemistry courses, I learned French and German, and took advanced courses in political science (i.e., Modern Political Ideologies, American Political Thought).

The time for hard decisions was at hand: a field of study, a career, and settling down. Batista was gone and Fidel Castro and his followers had established a revolutionary government committed to creating a new social and political order. It was not certain that my family, like many others, could survive in such a system. I was more and more doubtful that my future was in Cuba. And if my family needed my financial support, that would put an end to my plans for graduate work.

I was excited at the prospect of my last co-op job, which would last from summer through fall. As a senior, I had some leverage, and I ended up choosing a city rather than a job. Susan's descriptions of Boston, its history, its schools, its culture, had appealed to me. I decided to go with New England Nuclear Corporation in Boston. NENC was a start-up company that produced radioactive compounds used for research and clinical treatments. The job itself was only mildly interesting, combining quality testing, inventory, and shipping. On the other hand, there was Boston.

I fell in love with Boston. I rented a small studio apartment on the top floor of a row house on Beacon Hill just up the street from Louisburg Square. On Saturdays, I could walk down to Haymarket Square and shop for fresh meat, seafood and produce. With friends in graduate school at Harvard, I gained access to the rich academic life of Harvard and MIT. I attended all kinds of lectures and symposia. There were also books from the Boston Public Library, the art collections at the Museum of Fine Arts and Gardner Museum, and the rehearsals at the Boston Symphony. I also hoped against hope that Susan and I would get together again, but this never came to be.

This period was intellectually, culturally and socially rich. I found a good friend in Frank, my supervisor at NENC, who was just a few years older. In the process, I learned about the entrepreneurial nature of the US high tech industry. Frank was a bachelor whose salary was more than adequate. The company had a policy of profit sharing, and Frank used his savings and profit shares to buy stock in the company. A few years later, I learned that NENC was bought up by DuPont and many employees like Frank were able to sell their stock at a significant gain and go on to new positions. Even though I had only worked for six months for NENC, I was surprised to get a check for my share of the annual profits.

Boston was exhilarating, but I was happy at being able to go home for Christmas. It was an exciting period, with the revolutionary government firmly in power and moving rapidly to implement its new policies of agrarian, economic and educational reform. There was also uncertainty and doubt, particularly among the families of my friends. Most of them had supported the 26th of July movement but, as members of the middle class, were concerned about the erosion of civil liberties and harbored doubts about the growing power of the state over economic life. I was happy at seeing many of my old friends and was pleased at being at the wedding of Julia, one of my favorite classmates.

But there were unpredictable moments of sadness. For many of these young people, the revolution had interrupted their lives, and now they had to decide whether they would be able to go back to their studies and/or jobs. Many had become revolutionaries themselves. I recall a violent argument with Victor, the son of my godfather, who vehemently defended the right of the revolutionary government to carry out open trials of former members of the security services and the army, which often led to summary executions or paredon (the wall). He told me that I had no right to judge–I was one of those who had run away from the struggle. Rosita, a very pretty classmate and someone on whom I had had a crush, told me, "We of our generation have had to ignore our scruples and do some really dirty work. Now we have no choice but to be committed to the Revolution." I understood that we had grown up and our lives were headed down very different tracks. I did not know it then, but I would not see Cuba again for fifty years.

My last two quarters in Yellow Springs would stretch out to a year and a half and lead to decisions that deeply affected my future. When I felt tempted to switch majors and go into political science, my political science professor convinced me that my opportunities in America would be far better if I stayed in chemistry. Quite prophetically, he told me that if I did well in science, there would be future opportunities in policy. At the same time, my chemistry adviser kept trying to steer me towards inorganic chemistry, a field that I found less interesting. As luck would have it, one of my last chemistry courses, in biochemistry, finally got my attention. To understand life in terms of a vast variety of chemical reactions really sparked my curiosity. But did I want to pursue a graduate program in biochemistry purely on the basis of one course and the exciting lectures of one professor?

In the background was the persistent worry about my family. Letters from home indicated that Father wanted to move to the United States but could not figure out how to get US visas nor how to earn a living. And, though I was certain that I would go on to graduate school, I felt tired of school and wanted to help my family. I opted to take a year off and accept a position as a laboratory technician in the biochemistry lab of the Fels Research Institute in Yellow Springs.

As my undergraduate career was coming to an end, I launched into a frenzy of experimentation. Not only was I learning about biochemistry, but I started writing a column for the college newspaper, got elected to the Community Council and became its chair, wrote an essay for the literary magazine. For the first time, I even dated an Asian girl. One of my college buddies had worked on me to take out this lovely young woman from California. I finally gave in to his advice and asked her out. At the end of our first date, I asked her how fluent she was in Chinese. She admitted that she did not know Chinese. But then again, she told me, she was Korean not Chinese. I was struck dumb; my father (like others of his generation) believed that they could readily distinguish Chinese from Koreans and Japanese. But it really did not make any difference.

Father flew to Yellow Springs for my graduation. My Korean friend took us out to dinner at the college tea room (since she had extra meal tickets). My father was impressed because (a) I was finally going out with a Chinese girl and (b) she was attractive and charming. As with me, he was surprised to find out that she was Korean. Next day, Father told me that I should not be concerned that she was Korean. He fully approved of my choice.

The End of the Beginning

The Antioch years had been ones of excitement and discovery punctuated by moments of sadness and frustration. After graduation, I looked forward to a quiet year that would allow for rest and an opportunity to prepare myself for the next stage of my life. It did not at all turn out that way.

The year started with a youth leadership training camp called the Encampment for Citizenship run by the American Ethical Society at the University of California, Berkeley. The group brought together about fifty young people from a variety of backgrounds including Indian reservations, civil rights organizations, trade unions, Hispanic groups, my first exposure to totally different segments of American society. We had lectures and working sessions with various social and political activists.

I had never been to California before and I just loved the weeks spent wandering around Berkeley, San Francisco, and Palo Alto. I dated a girl from Pasadena and was able to spend time in the Caltech area, experiencing first hand another center of US high technology. The most important learning of that summer involved living and working with strongly motivated youths from very different backgrounds. But things were due to change rapidly as the summer drew to an end and I headed for Yellow Springs and my new job.

In the meantime, Castro's government had developed close ties to the Chinese Communist government, which planned on spreading its version of Marxism in Latin America. Chinese operatives had approached my father and tried to recruit him. As a committed anticommunist, he would never work for the regime in Beijing. Cuban friends in the Castro government advised him to leave immediately and have my mother and sister join him later. Father left for New York. He asked me to send him the funds that he had brought during my graduation. Part of it would be to support him while he tried to find a job. The remainder was to be used to get Mother and Rosie out of Cuba.

But the money had already been spent on the debts incurred in my last year of college. I did not know what to do. This was a moment of complete paralysis: new job, new apartment, just a few dollars in my bank account. I had no idea how to come up with money for my family. I experienced the deep sense of desperation that comes from realizing that there is very little you can do to help your family when you have neither money nor influential contacts. In the end, I went for advice to the dean of students at Antioch who was able to provide me with a loan. Father searched for a job in New York and we worked on getting Mother and Rosie out of Havana.

On a cool afternoon in November, 1960, Mother and Rosie landed in the airport in Dayton. The chilly fall weather was in sharp contrast to the tropical breezes of the Caribbean. Mother was in control as always, but 15-year-old Rosie was crushed and could not think of anything except going home. Mother stayed just for a few days before she joined Father in New York. They had decided that New York was not a good place for Rosie, and that she should stay with me in Yellow Springs. I was to arrange for her living and school arrangements.

Once again, I was at a total loss. My plans had been to settle into a new job and become familiar with biochemistry concepts and techniques, put my finances in order, and organize myself to go on with graduate school. Instead, my top priority was to take care of my kid sister. The small one-bedroom apartment that I shared with Peter was too small for the three of us. But we were fortunate in that Yellow Springs was exceptionally open and generous for displaced people like us. The family of an engineering professor who had a daughter Rosie's age was glad to take her in. As a resident of the village, the high school would accept her as a local student and would waive any special fees or tuition.

Working at the Fels Institute turned out to be a real introduction to modern biology. The Institute was dedicated to a longitudinal study on human development. A major portion of it looked at changes in behavior and learning as a select group of subjects went from infancy to adulthood. There was a great deal of work done on physical and physiological development. Our biochemistry laboratory followed certain biochemical markers and tried to determine whether their levels in the human body were primarily due to genetic factors or to environmental elements such as nutrition and growth. The laboratory was headed by a well-known biochemist, but most of my time was spent with two very skillful Japanese scientists. I started off by carrying out analyses of urine samples and then moved on to the synthesis of some of the metabolites we were measuring in our subjects. The lab was a marvelously peaceful place on the edge of the campus and an easy ten-minute walk from our apartment. Aside from my regular schedule, I spent most of my evenings and weekends in the lab. Peter worked equally hard, but both of us tried to spend time with Rosie, who was trying to adjust to life in America.

As winter turned to spring, things began to fall into place. I had become increasingly fascinated by the puzzle of life and the possibility that it could be understood in chemical terms. The next step was to decide on where to pursue advanced studies. At the same time, I was still fascinated by alternatives to a scientific career. On one hand, there was the possibility of doing graduate work in Latin American Studies. Another alternative was to go into a program studying agricultural economics and development in Sweden. Once again, fate stepped in, this time in the form of the father of one of my classmates.

Bernard Horecker was a well established biochemist who had been a noted lab chief at the National Institutes of Health, then moved on to become chair of Microbiology at the New York University School of Medicine. He was keen to recruit students for his graduate program. Early one Sunday morning, there was a knock at the door. A well-dressed gentleman, introducing himself as Dr. Horecker, wondered whether we might have a conversation. I was totally overwhelmed, but tried desperately to wake up and sound scientifically literate. He was friendly and did a fine job of describing his vision for the new department. A few weeks later, I decided to go to NYU and to have Horecker as my mentor. The fact that I would be able to live with my parents and help with the family finances was central to my decision.

The Antioch years introduced me to all kinds of complexities of American life. While its campus was, at the time, lacking in student and cultural diversity, the co-op experience took me to different parts of the country for a variety of jobs. Susan exposed me to a large body of literature that broadened my love of the language and my sense of country and culture. And, while I had received a solid grounding in science, I had the opportunity to explore my interests in political science, global affairs, and foreign languages. Taken as a whole, it began to seem highly unlikely that I would return to Cuba.

Before I left Yellow Springs, there was one more task to be done. Rosie had adjusted to school and life in Yellow Springs, but there were frictions with her host family. They had suggested to me that it would be best for them and for her to find another home. Luckily, one of my best friends was from Yellow Springs and I arranged it for Rosie to move in with them. They were a solid, warmhearted Quaker family with three sons. She became like a daughter to the parents and a sister to the young sons. I felt comfortable leaving her in Yellow Springs.

I spent six years off and on in Yellow Springs. For me, it will always be a special place, where some fundamental dreams and values were formed. What had started out six years earlier as just a decision to go to college abroad had resulted in my whole family finding a home in the United States.

Rose and Tao-Feng at their wedding in Nanking October 1936

Rose, age 20, just before her marriage to Tao-Feng

Our family in Cuba the year I graduated high school 1952

View of the
Capitol
Havana

The apartment home
of the author
Havana

Main Hall,
Antioch College

Yellow Springs,
Glen Helen
Antioch College

Old friends at
Antioch College

Harvard
Biological Labs
Cambridge,
Massachusetts

Dr. Matt Meselson,
molecular biologist
Harvard University

Moray Place
Edinburgh

Nobel Laureate
Werner Arber and
Noreen Murray

Darwin Tower
Edinburgh
University

THE PURSUIT OF SCIENCE
Manhattan - Cambridge - Edinburgh
1961-1970

Antioch had done an exceptional job of preparing me for an emerging world reshaped by new technologies and growing connections between nations and cultures. What it had not prepared me for were the frustrations and uncertainties of graduate education. These challenges were associated with the birth of a new scientific field.

Transitions

It was the fall of 1961, and the transition from an undergraduate education at a liberal arts college in Ohio to a PhD program at a major medical school in New York City was bumpy. Most graduate students at NYU enrolled in the graduate school of arts and sciences located on the main campus of the university. A small number of students enrolled in basic medical sciences at the medical school. Medical schools are dedicated to biomedical research, clinical services, and training of medical students. The graduate departments focused on research to which PhD training was peripheral.

The difference between programs on the main campus and programs at the medical school almost brought my academic career to an early end. In my casual examination of the graduate catalog, I had noted that the fall semester of the graduate school began in the third week of September. I used the medical school catalog to choose the courses for my first semester. I decided that if I arrived in mid-September, I would have plenty of time to settle in and get started with my courses. When I showed up, I got yelled at by everyone, starting with the departmental secretary and the teaching assistants. While the graduate school did start in the third week of September, medical school started the day after Labor Day, as did the graduate program in basic medical sciences! I was ten days late. Not an auspicious beginning.

For the first three semesters, graduate students took many of the preclinical basic science courses (i.e., biochemistry, physiology, microbiology) with the medical students. Being among a handful of graduate students in a sea of medical students was daunting. The courses, encompassing a combination of research topics and medical applications (e.g., blood chemistry, glucose utilization), were taught by a faculty team. A fundamental aspect of medical education was the memorization of vast amounts of material and its regurgitation in an endless series of quizzes and examinations. The principal strategy for survival was to find a (hopefully congenial) group of medical students with whom to share class notes, readings, and cram sessions. This led to the discovery that the culture of medical students was distinctive, nothing like the experiential approach and supportive learning community at Antioch.

It was obvious that the graduate program was an appendage of a high-powered research unit composed of faculty, researchers and technicians. Many of the researchers were research fellows with PhDs or M.D.s. In a department of seventy to eighty, there were only a dozen graduate students and only one other graduate student in my entering class. To the faculty, graduate students did not exist until they started research on their thesis projects.

This was the first time I encountered big time academic politics. Dr. Bernard Horecker had taken over the Department of Microbiology, traditionally the study of bacteria and viruses and their roles in disease. However, he and the group of young faculty and researchers he had recruited were really biochemists positioning themselves to launch the new field of molecular biology. The problem was that NYU already had a famous Department of Biochemistry led by Dr. Severo Ochoa, a Nobel Prize laureate, brilliant, proud, and with the temperament of a grandee of Spain. He did not take kindly to the idea of the Department of Microbiology poaching on his territory, in terms of both research and teaching.

As students, we were particularly sensitive to the tensions between the two departments since we had to take courses in both departments. The tensions continued to escalate until my second year at NYU, when Horecker decided to move his department to the Albert Einstein College of Medicine located in the Bronx. To accommodate the plans of Horecker and his colleagues, Einstein created a Department of Molecular Biology with new laboratories and state-of-the-art equipment. Students like myself who had completed their two years of course work were given the choice to transfer to the new department. The choice was really no choice in that you could not but follow your mentor.

The transition from the small village of Yellow Springs to the metropolis of New York tested my resilience and ability to adapt. The intellectual and social environment of a liberal arts college in no way resembled that of a biomedical research complex with no campus life. At the outset, I found an apartment near Brooklyn Heights which I shared with my parents. My father had struggled for a long time before he eventually got a position as an evening librarian at the NYU Medical School. My mother had been more fortunate in becoming a waitress at the Summit Hotel downtown. Until Father got his job, we survived on my mother's income and my meager fellowship. Our disparate schedules and work locations meant that most often we did not see much of each other except on weekends.

We lived in two worlds: my father still thought and acted as a gentleman and a diplomat, while Mother and I lived the lives of immigrants and did what we had to do. Even though I had my own room, I found it increasingly difficult to have any privacy and to live in a family environment after being on my own for so long. Questions about my time management and my social life became harder and harder to handle. Once my father got his job, I decided that it was time for me to find my own place.

Apartments in New York were precious, and the holy grail was a rent-controlled apartment. My first task was to find a roommate with whom I could share the rent. Michael Tsien, a friend from the Encampment for Citizenship, had just graduated from Purdue and arrived in New York in search of a job. We found a one bedroom apartment near Columbia University, and he made the rounds of possible employers. I liked the neighborhood with its small shops, restaurants and student hangouts. One of these was the Brass Rail, a place for late night beers after I had done my course readings and assignments. I was not about to give all of this up when my department moved north to the suburban quietude of the Bronx. Life became more complicated when Michael could not find a job in New York and left to take up a position with Ford in Detroit. What next?? A new postdoc,

Peter McNamara, also had little desire to live in the Bronx, so I convinced him to share a two bedroom apartment in the Columbia neighborhood. This arrangement worked out well except for the lengthy commute to the Einstein and the need to coordinate our schedules.

New York was expensive. Shaping a social life required ingenuity and hard work. Developing a close circle of friends was key. First, there were Antioch graduates who were either in graduate school or had jobs. Through them, it became possible to meet others in that fluid bohemian scene of the 1960s. There were musicians, social workers, union organizers, journalists. All of this provided a rich counterpoint to the hard grind of thesis research. There were ample opportunities to meet young women who were working or studying in the city. Ironically, the most important of all these relationships involved Michael. Being relatively close in age, Michael, my sister Rosie and I used to hang out together. It was a standard joke that Michael should date Rosie, something that never happened. Michael, on the other hand, had a sister, Ying-Ying, who seldom went out with us but who would eventually change everything.

The Slog

The academic departments have two basic approaches in choosing topics for PhD theses. One approach involves stand-alone problems which are removed from the fierce competition of research groups and provide opportunities to learn a broad spectrum of techniques. The other selects a part of a major group research project, which makes the topic both more exciting and more risky. I chose to explore a stand-alone problem. My thesis detailed the study of the chemical composition and structure of the cell wall of an obscure Brazilian fungus. My chemistry background was particularly suited to the project even though I knew little about polysaccharides. The project was laborious and tedious in that it required growing large amounts of the fungus, purifying the polysaccharides from the cell wall, and then breaking it down to smaller components that could be chemically analyzed. This was not easy since the polysaccharide was hard to break down. After more than two years, I was confident that I had been able to purify the major polysaccharide of this fungal cell wall and established its chemical composition and structure.

The next stage of my career required a postdoctoral position at a major research institution and a fellowship to support me. I knew that I wanted to move in the direction of DNA research, which sharply limited the number of possible laboratories and mentors. For strong personal reasons, I had decided to go to Boston and had applied to three laboratories there: D.G. Fraenkel's at the Harvard Medical School, B. Magasanik's at MIT, and Matthew Meselson's at Harvard's Biological Laboratories.

Most of my professors and researchers considered Meselson to be one of the most brilliant molecular biologists around, well known for the elegance of his experiments and their resulting papers. However, I was warned that he was difficult to get along with and that it was very hard to gain a position in his laboratory. In order to gain access to him, I was dependent on the support of Horecker and Jerry Hurwitz, a well-known nucleic acid biochemist in my department. I met Meselson at a conference in New York and visited his laboratory in Cambridge. I found him to be polite and soft spoken, endowed with a quick intelligence. I was surprised and thrilled when I learned that I had been accepted to work in his lab.

Things seemed to be falling into place. I had begun writing my thesis starting with a review of the literature on fungal cell walls. Doing literature searches, I discovered a new paper that described a method for purifying polysaccharides based on their electrical charge. In what I had hoped to be a last set of experiments, I tried the new method and was horrified to learn that what I had believed to be a single species of fungal polysaccharide was actually a mixture of two distinct polysaccharides. This meant that most of my data was useless and that the work would have to be repeated on each of the two cell wall polysaccharides. This was a crushing moment since it was early fall and I had planned on finishing my thesis by the next summer and taking up my postdoctoral fellowship in Boston in September. I was not going to make it!

When I told Horecker, he was supportive and sympathetic. He gave me two options: to continue with the project (which would probably take one more year) or to take part in a group project that was determining the biochemical pathway for the synthesis of the cell wall of the bacteria, Salmonella Typhimurium. In the latter case, I would be responsible for determining the early steps in the pathway. No one knew how long this would take. Tired of working on the Brazilian fungus, I decided to join the group working on S. Typhimurium.

As I familiarized myself with the Salmonella project, I realized that much of the information had been obtained from a collection of mutants, each of which was blocked at a separate synthesis step. If I were to use the same approach, it would take a long time. So I gambled on using crude bacterial extracts and synchronizing and stopping the individual reactions. The results were promising, and after that it became a race against time to generate the results necessary for the thesis. The mad dash enabled me to complete the experiments by the early spring and write my doctoral thesis by June, 1966.

Though I was well grounded in biochemistry, my experience in the genetics of viruses and bacteria and molecular techniques was limited. I decided to take two intensive research courses at the famed Cold Spring Harbor Laboratory located in Long Island. There I took the Bacterial Genetics course taught by John Beckwith and John Scaife along with Julian Gross of the University of Edinburgh and the Phage Genetics course taught by Frances Womack of the Oak Ridge National Laboratory and Millard Sussman of the University of Wisconsin, Madison. At the end of this sprint was my thesis defense in August, 1966.

That summer was one of the fullest in my life with a combination of intellectual intensity, lively socializing, and youthful romance. The summer population of Cold Spring Harbor was richly diverse with well established names, aspiring young scientists, and plenty of technicians and support staff. Each summer there was a major symposium that focused on a major topic (e.g., DNA replication), attracting researchers from all over the world. Then there were those that came to work in the labs or collaborated on the writing of papers. And finally, there were those who came to attend the advanced courses. It all came together in the unique environment of Cold Spring Harbor with its combination of lectures, experiments, discussions, and shared meals and parties (lubricated by a generous supply of alcohol). I met many people at CSH who would become partners in research in future years.

More Transitions

As the graduate years went by, my relationship with Ying-Ying intensified. She was pursuing her undergraduate studies in anthropology at Bryn Mawr, but she came up to New York on weekends. She managed to finish her AB in three years and decided to go on to New Hall, Cambridge University, for her PhD. This was almost a natural move since her mother had received her BA in physics from London University and her father had gone to Kings College, Cambridge, for his MA in physics. She left for Cambridge in 1965. I left for Harvard in September 1966, almost five years to the day after I had arrived in New York from Antioch to begin my graduate work. I was excited to join Meselson's lab. Soon afterwards, Ying joined me at Harvard.

Harvard: The Rhinos at the Gates

Even though I had a deep interest in international affairs and diplomacy, I had followed my father's advice to pursue a career in science. Science was exciting and would provide me with a way to earn a living regardless of my country of residence. My undergraduate training in chemistry had led me to a PhD in molecular biology. Now the years at Harvard led me to research on how DNA could be cleaved into defined segments. Science brought me to Europe and beyond. Work in a new field was to provide me with broader international opportunities.

I was poised to start my scientific career in one of the most prestigious biology research laboratories in the world. I was glad to leave New York and move to Cambridge. But my high expectations were tempered by a concern that I might not be up to the challenges ahead. Matt Meselson was one of the founding fathers of molecular biology and had become a full professor at Harvard at the age of 30. He was 38 when I joined his group and was widely respected for the clarity of his thinking, the elegance of his experiments, and the classical nature of his scientific papers. His approach was to take an important and complex biological question, formulate it in a cogent and unambiguous fashion, then design a set of experiments (with the appropriate controls) that could answer the question in only one of two possible ways. In this manner, he had made major contributions to our understanding of two fundamental biological phenomena: DNA replication and DNA recombination.

Space was my first concern: a place to live, a lab to work. The first need was satisfied by a small one-bedroom apartment on Harvard Street an easy fifteen-minute walk to the Biological Laboratories on Divinity Avenue. A Damon Runyon fellowship supported my modest needs. Given the crowded state of Meselson's laboratories, lab space was hard to come by. I ended up in the grad students' lab with a large table without lab fixtures or faucets, but with a grand view of the courtyard and the entrance to the Bio Labs, guarded by two monumental bronze rhinos named Bessie and Vicky after the British monarchs. Meselson instructed me to use the lab bench assigned to one graduate student, Vincenzo Pirrotta, who was hardly ever there. Vincenzo did not take kindly to a squatter on his space, which made for an inauspicious start to my postdoctoral fellowship.

Many members of Meselson's laboratory were senior investigators (often on leave from their universities) who applied his intellectual and experimental tools in the pursuit of their own projects. Among them were Kenichi Matsubara from Osaka University, Theo Staehelin from the University of Michigan, and Toshio Nagata from Tokyo. There were two other postdoctoral fellows of my age, Marc Rhoades and Sidney Altman (who went on to share in the 1989 Nobel Prize in Chemistry). The presence of such experienced investigators made me feel ignorant and insecure. This was not necessarily helped by the fact that Meselson assumed that most of his collaborators knew as much as he did and shared his ideas at a rapid pace.

In the first of many such meetings, I went into his large office to discuss possible projects. I lit up a cigarillo and took copious notes only to be interrupted by Meselson who asked whether I had an extra cigarillo. After talking for a couple of hours, he asked whether I liked seafood. When I replied in the affirmative, he suggested we adjourn for lunch at Legal Seafoods, a downtown staple which was to become an institution not only in Boston but throughout the country. Once there, he asked whether I had enough cash on me, which I did. It was not unusual for Meselson to take us out, but we might have to advance him the money.

Meselson gave me a choice of two projects. The first was a study of the mechanism of recombination in a bacterial virus. Alternatively, I could study the biological phenomenon known as restriction and modification. Though many well-known scientists had studied this phenomenon (including Meselson himself), the actual nature of some of the specific reactions was unknown. I was attracted to this project, though it had the serious disadvantage that no one else in the Bio Labs was working on it. On the plus side, Meselson was fascinated by the problem and had decided to spend his upcoming sabbatical in place and, if I chose to work on it, we would do it together. That was an exciting prospect.

Working so closely with Meselson was one of those once-in-a-lifetime experiences. For weeks and weeks, I read through everything that had been published on restriction and modification, and there was much. Bacteria are able to transfer DNA from one cell to another through a variety of mechanisms. It had been observed that if the cells exchanging DNA were from the same strain, the exchange would take place without hindrance and recombination could then take place. However, if the DNA was transferred from cells of one strain to cells of a different strain, the DNA would be restricted (destroyed) by the recipient cell. This meant that a cell could distinguish between self and non-self at the molecular level of the DNA. There was also evidence that such cells were also able to mark their own DNA identifying its origin. This process was called modification and involved the incorporation of methyl groups onto the DNA. From a biological viewpoint, a living cell would safeguard the integrity of its genetic heritage by destroying foreign DNA while at the same time protecting its own DNA.

We started out by looking at two possible systems: the one from a standard bacteria strain, E. coli K12 (EcoK) and the other from the phage P1 (EcoP1). It must be remembered that at that time, while there was biological evidence for the existence of restriction endonucleases, enzymes that specifically destroyed foreign, unmodified DNA had not been actually detected and isolated. The bacterial strains contained a number of non-specific enzymes, so the key to the puzzle was to establish an assay that could detect the specific activity of the restriction endonucleases. There were two possible assays: a biological assay using a mixture of two phages (one modified, the other unmodified) carrying different genes or alternatively, a biophysical method using a mixture of two DNAs (one modified, one unmodified) differentially labeled with the radioactive isotopes carbon-14 and phosphorus-32. In the case of the first, the phage mixture would be incubated with the appropriate cellular extract and then be used to infect host cells. In the case of the second, the mixture of DNAs was centrifuged in a neutral sucrose gradient. If the restriction endonuclease was present, it would be detected by either the preferential loss of biological activity or breaks in the unmodified DNA (with no concurrent action on the modified DNA).

The Hunt for the Restriction Endonuclease

That first autumn was an exercise in frustration. I would have become convinced of my ineptitude with matters of DNA had it not been for the fact that Meselson was not doing any better. My senior colleagues such as Kenichi and Theo provided moral support and expert technical advice. The assays were laborious, took days, frequently going late into the night. And then there was the tedium of analyzing the data. The assays were not working, the infectivity assays showed loss of activity by both DNAs while there was no evidence of endonuclease activity in the gradient assays. Was the problem with the assays or the extract preparation? Meselson then hypothesized that the reaction required energy and suggested the addition of ATP (the biological molecule used for energy transfer) to the extract. All of a sudden, almost unbelievably, there it was, a specific activity that cleaved the unmodified DNA but not the modified one.

But the task was not going to be that simple. As we began the enzyme purification, the activity disappeared with or without ATP. The critical clue lay in a single line at the conclusion of a paper by Bill Wood describing work done in Geneva. He had observed that restriction required an amino acid called methionine.

Inside bacterial cells there is a reaction that combines methionine and ATP to make an unusual compound called S-adenosylmethionine (AdoMet). Up to this point, AdoMet's metabolic role was that of a methyl donor in methylation reactions. It became clear that this novel endonuclease activity required ATP, AdoMet and Mg++. While both EcoK and EcoP1 seemed to share the same characteristics, we decided to concentrate on the purification of EcoK since much more was known about the genetics of that system. Armed with an effective (though laborious) assay and knowledge of its cofactors, EcoK was purified to homogeneity by the spring of 1967.

Ordinarily, we would have raced to publish our results because of their significance. But such a move would have gone against Meselson's concept of a classical paper that would provide a clear answer to a major scientific question. So for the better part of another year, we purified EcoP1 in order to compare these two enzymes, then determined the size of the fragments produced by EcoK, and its actions on three distinct types of DNA, modified, unmodified, and hybrid (one strand modified, one unmodified).

The scientific world was filled with rumors and gossip about this first restriction enzyme. I was a fellow of the Helen Hay Whitney Foundation which supported me for three years. The Foundation held an annual meeting in Princeton for its fellows and the members of its scientific committee. One of the principal purposes of this weekend was to allow senior investigators and young fellows to interact intellectually and socially in an elegant setting. Second year fellows were required to present talks on their projects.

On the first evening, I joined the welcoming cocktail party feeling lost since I knew no one in the group of fifty or so participants. I joined a small group that was clustered around Norton Zinder, a professor at the Rockefeller Institute. There was an excited buzz that Meselson's lab had discovered and purified the restriction endonuclease, but no one seemed to know this for a fact or have any details. Then one of the senior fellows from U.C. Berkeley took over the conversation and began to speak authoritatively about the Meselson experiments. I stood in utter silence while my heart pounded away. This fellow was talking about our experiments, but he had it all wrong! A lifetime seemed to go by while I tried to decide whether to speak up. Finally, I cleared my throat, and softly said, "Excuse me, but I do not think that you have that quite right."

He glared back at me. "And who are you?" he asked.

I responded, "You are talking about my work." Suddenly, I had the floor. Despite struggling with a dry mouth and a squeaky voice, I went on to share the excitement of our discovery.

Many years later, I was serving on a scientific advisory committee in Taiwan. During a break, I was chatting with another committee member, Chua Nam Hai, a professor at the Rockefeller University. Suddenly, he asked me whether I remembered him. I answered affirmatively since we had met at various conferences. He said, "No, I mean at Harvard." I had to admit that I did not recall him from that period. He told me that he was an honors student at the Bio Labs when I was a fellow, one of the few Chinese there at that time. The rules required us to sign in and out any time after 6 p.m. and before 7 am. When he realized that I spent most nights in the labs, I became one of his role models.

The Nature 1968 Paper

The paper on EcoK was published in the March, 1968 issue of Nature. It described the purification of both EcoK and EcoP1 and characterized the mechanism of action of EcoK: a restriction endonuclease that cleaved first one strand, then the opposite one, but did not make any cuts on heteroduplex DNA (one strand modified and one unmodified). The DNA digest was unusual in that not all restriction sites were cleaved. Given the rather unusual requirements of EcoK, the paper suggested (but did not prove) that the same enzyme might also be responsible for DNA modification. The publication of the EcoK paper coincided with that of EcoB by Stuart Linn and Werner Arber in the Proceedings of the National Academy of Sciences.

The Nature paper received a great deal of attention and eventually led to the technology that cuts DNA into defined segments. The availability of restriction endonucleases led to the mapping and sequencing of DNA and, most importantly of all, to the cutting and splicing of DNA genes into heterologous chromosomes. These technical procedures represent what we call "genetic engineering," which enables scientists to change the genetic makeup of any living cell. Genetic engineering is a major component of biotechnology (i.e., the technological applications of biology). It is an irony of history that all the work we had done on the restriction systems of EcoK and the phage P1 could not be used for genetic engineering. These enzymes belong to a family called Type I, which were complex and did not cut DNA at precise sites.

In 1970, Hamilton Smith and Tom Kelly published a paper in which they described an enzyme from Haemophilus influenzae that belonged to the Type II family, a family which efficiently cut DNA at specified sites. Type II enzymes became the essential tools for biotechnology. The study of restriction and modification illustrated the linkage between new knowledge and its transformation into a series of enabling technologies that led to a multiplicity of new products and applications. The early work of Arber, Boyer, and Wood centered on understanding how cells control the transfer of DNA from one cell to another. On its own, this knowledge is of limited practical use. But when it was followed by the more molecular approach from our laboratory as well as those of Arber, Linn, Boyer, and Smith, this new understanding opened a brave new world that resulted in the sequencing of DNA and the construction of novel DNA molecules (and therefore of modified living cells).

The Bio Labs were a beehive of research activity, one which combined icons of the golden age of biochemistry such as the

Nobel Laureates George Wald and Konrad Bloch with the new wave of molecular biologists such as James Watson and Walter Gilbert. Watson was one of its most influential members who, with Francis Crick, had determined the structure of DNA and who had written the bestselling books *The Double Helix* and *The Molecular Biology of the Gene*. The first explained to the public the life and challenges of basic research, while the second became the textbook on molecular biology. The Bio Labs were the breeding ground for many young molecular biologists who trained there as graduate students such as Mark Ptashne, Joan Argetsinger, Dick Burgess, Vincenzo Pirrotta, and postdoctoral fellows such as Sydney Altman and Miroslav Radman.

Science, Politics and Love

Meselson told me that there were only three things that were truly worth doing: "science, politics and love." Working with him in the lab, I had experienced the excitement of scientific research. Now I began to observe how science can be applied to shape policy.

As a practical matter, I had limited control over my future. I had a Taiwan passport and a student visa that expired when I completed my PhD. The US had an immigration policy based on national origins which limited the number of Chinese immigrants to several hundred applicants per year. The 1965 immigration reform law passed by the Johnson administration had replaced the national origins criteria with more liberal ones based on family relationships and occupational priorities. In my request for permanent residence, I used my PhD in Molecular Biology as the basis for my application. The immigration officer was totally baffled by this mysterious field that did not appear in his long list of occupations. However, he noticed that my undergraduate degree was in Chemistry, "and that will certainly do." I progressed to a permanent resident's green card, which would ultimately make me eligible for citizenship. However, a Taiwanese passport was of very limited use as a travel document since by then only the US, the Vatican, and a handful of Central American and African countries recognized Taiwan.

In the late 1960s, the US escalated its military intervention in South Vietnam. The opposition to the war increased and spilled over into American campuses, and Harvard was no exception. In Meselson's laboratory, antiwar sentiment took various forms: long arguments in the tea room, petitions to Congress, attendance at teach-ins, and finally, impassioned demonstrations on the campus. Meselson's approach to politics was dramatically different from that of most other research scientists. He steered away from the ideology and polemics of opposition to the war and focused on a major policy issue that affected arms control and peace negotiations. This was the development and use of chemical and biological weapons.

While nuclear weapons and their delivery systems were the monopoly of a small number of major powers, chemical and biological weapons (CBW) were considered the "poor man's nuclear weapons." CBW represented a major danger in that if the US and the USS.R. pushed the development of these weapons, it would further complicate arms control negotiations. Perhaps even more dangerous was the possibility that unstable regimes would use them in local or regional conflicts, which could rapidly escalate out of control. Meselson had begun his involvement in CBW during a year spent in the Arms Control and Disarmament Agency. He had been an active participant in the Pugwash conferences, which brought together top scientists from the US and the USSR to discuss issues of arms control.

He had retained his high-level security clearance, his contacts, and his access to a large body of scientific information. In the process, he acquired a double identity as a member of the establishment and as a neutral academic expert dedicated to the analysis of biological weapons. Even though he believed in the moral imperative of limiting weapons competition, his approach was to convince policy makers that biological weapons provided few advantages to the defense establishments of major powers but could encourage the proliferation of this type of mass weapons among developing countries. His mastery of facts and his detailed analysis played an important role in President Nixon's review of the US CBW programs. This led to the suspension of CBW weapons production and then to the 1972 Geneva Convention which prohibited the development, production, acquisition, and transfer of biological agents and toxins.

Meselson became, to me, a model of someone who could apply many of the same methods of rigorous analysis in scientific research to fundamental issues of government policy. There were mixed feelings in the scientific community regarding Meselson's involvement in arms policy. Some were strongly supportive of the idea that scientists should have significant input on how technology should be used. Others took the position that leading scientists should stay focused on their science and restrict themselves to research and teaching.

In Good Company

I had not forgotten Meselson's list: "science, politics, and love." Another aspect of those Cambridge years was the richness of its social life. While Boston had plenty of establishments for drinking and dancing, they closed early. So around Harvard, much of the social life centered around dinners and parties at people's homes. Both Meselson and I were bachelors at the time, so we would go out together with our girlfriends. At a time when Julia Child was creating a culture of haute cuisine on the East Coast, we enjoyed all kinds of food and wine. We were glad to take a break from the long days of enzyme purification and restriction assays to cook and then go dancing at one of the local discos.

There were certain faculty members known for the liveliness of their parties, chief among them being Jim Watson. Such parties were characterized by an abundance of liquor, loud live music and, perhaps most striking of all, guests that included all kinds of intellectual luminaries: biologists such as George Wald, economists such as John Galbraith, and defense intellectuals such as George Kistiakowsky. At the same time, there was an abundance of young research scientists like myself and attractive young women from Radcliffe and Harvard.

The ethos of Cambridge in those years was one in which we worked very hard in cutting-edge fields and at the same time, we were supposed to have a social life that was equally vibrant and exciting. I was also fortunate in that Ying-Ying, an anthropologist, got us invited to parties in the Department of Social Relations with a whole different cast of characters, most of them involved in cognitive studies, human development, and anthropology. I had to admit that the SocRel parties at William James Hall were hard to match. Besides the Harvard world, we had other social networks. My sister, Rosie, was doing graduate work at B.U. and was dating Sung-Hou Kim, a crystallographer in the lab of Alex Rich at M.I.T. We also had friends from Antioch (Bob Dickerman, a foreign service officer; Ed Bing, an architect). If the weather was good, we would spend long days at Crane Beach or Cape Cod.

My relationship with Ying-Ying was deepening. Though I had seldom dated Chinese or Asian women, here I was in a very traditional situation. I had shared an apartment in New York with Ying's brother, Michael, and he was one of my oldest friends. Ying's grandfather was Wellington Koo, one of modern China's most renowned diplomats and statesmen and a mentor of my father when he joined the foreign service. Ying's mother, Patricia, was a senior U.N. official charged with the decolonization of Portuguese colonies in Africa. So our families had a common history, including a deep involvement in diplomacy and foreign policy. We were to have an exciting wedding in June, 1967, that included a service at the U.N. chapel presided over by the Rev. Donald Harrington, an elaborate Chinese banquet, and a night of dancing at the Cheetah discotheque.

Into the World

For more than a decade, I had lived and studied in the United States with the occasional trip home to Havana. Unlike many of my classmates, I lacked the funds to travel abroad and my Taiwanese passport was not valid for travel to many countries. But now, with the publication of the Nature paper, this changed. In 1968, I was invited to attend a NATO conference in Bergen, Norway. I took that opportunity to stop in Geneva where I had been invited to speak to Werner Arber's department. I not only got to know Arber, but was also pleased to meet one of my other competitors (and collaborators), Stuart Linn, who had come from U.C. Berkeley to do his postdoctoral fellowship with Arber. Almost overnight, my network of scientific contacts expanded beyond the United States to Europe. After that first trip, in spite of spartan stipends and the complexities of traveling with Taiwanese passports, yearly summer trips to Europe became a part of our routine.

The Cambridge years represented a balance of our two careers. My two fellowships allowed me to pursue my research with Meselson for four years without the distractions of teaching and administrative work that are an essential part of faculty life. Over that same time, Ying-Ying had completed her courses and other PhD requirements and was moving on to her thesis research on the socialization of African women as they moved from the bush to the cities. The plan was that she would have completed all her PhD requirements except for the writing of her thesis when we moved on to our next jobs.

As the 1960s were coming to an end, it was time to think seriously about my future career. The circumstances were favorable in that molecular biology was a burgeoning new field, universities were expanding at a rapid pace, and I was coming out of one of the best labs in the world with a solid series of publications. At the same time, I was not much of a careerist, had not given serious thought to the different options and, as good as he was at science and policy, Meselson was not a very good counselor on such matters. So far, my experience in America was in highly intellectual and liberal enclaves such as New York and Boston, but most of the new positions were in large state universities in the South, the Midwest and the West. Ying-Ying and I had to get serious and do our homework to find permanent positions.

When Ying-Ying completed her course work, she began to formulate her thesis project. Given the work of her advisor, John Whiting, this would normally have involved two years of field work in Kenya. Whiting tried to convince me to take up a research appointment at University College, Nairobi, but that would not have done much for my research career. So Ying decided to spend three months doing field work in Kenya in the summer of 1969, and I would join her there for three weeks.

En route to Nairobi, I stopped in Geneva, where Arber had organized a small international conference on restriction and modification. By then I knew Werner fairly well and found him to be a fine, thorough scientist, serious and considerate in his relationships with other researchers. On the evening after the conference, he hosted a small dinner by the shores of Lake Geneva. After a relaxed and civilized meal, he suddenly asked me whether I had ever considered a job in Europe. Or even more specifically, would I consider a job in Switzerland? I had no answer since I had never thought of it. Werner explained that Edouard Kellenberger, one of the senior professors at Geneva, had convinced the canton of Basel to establish a new research institute, the Biozentrum, at the University of Basel. Kellenberger would be the chair of the Department of Microbiology and Werner would be a professor there in charge of molecular genetics research. There would be new junior positions, and Werner was keen to recruit me to join him in Basel. I was excited, but this was not a decision to be taken lightly. As my Swissair flight winged its way through the night towards Nairobi, I thought that this would be a big surprise for my wife and that we would have a great deal to discuss in the weeks ahead.

Big Decisions

Moving to Europe would have major implications for our careers and personal lives. Most of my American colleagues were adamant in their view that the US was the center of molecular biology research and that going to Europe would be damaging to my career. This was somewhat balanced by an established tradition in which young American scientists spent some time in the principal European universities at some point in their careers. Separately, there were the questions of how Ying would be able to complete her PhD and find an appropriate occupation in Switzerland.

Our immigration status further complicated matters. If we remained in the US, we were on track to get our US citizenship within three years. Not only would we have to negotiate our work/residency status in Switzerland, but our acquisition of US citizenship would be set back indefinitely. And what about starting a family? A baby born in Switzerland did not have a right to Swiss citizenship, which meant that he/she would be in the same legal limbo as we were. And then there was the timing. It was 1970, and the building and equipping of the Biozentrum would not be completed until the beginning of 1972. What would I do for the intervening year?

One advantageous factor was that Arber was on sabbatical at Berkeley, which allowed us to have extensive discussions. We visited Basel in the fall of 1970. Being one of the first candidates for the faculty of the new institute, cantonal government officials and senior faculty involved in the organization of the Biozentrum rolled out the red carpet for us. Every effort was made to highlight the attractions of a move to Basel. Even though Basel was smaller than Zurich or Geneva, it was an international center for both the pharmaceutical industry and for banking, making it one of the richest cities in the world. There was a commitment to make the Biozentrum one of the principal centers for biological research, with staff recruited from all over the world. Aside from emphasizing all the resources available to researchers (including highly competitive salaries and research support), the organizers did their best to give us a sense of the high quality of life. Work permits and residency papers were simply administrative matters that would be taken care of. They also invested a significant effort in wooing Ying, and made the commitment to help her find an appropriate place for her academic career. There were Swiss chocolates, elegant dinners, and bouquets of flowers.

Most important of all, they gave ample proof of the hardheaded pragmatism that characterizes the Swiss. Lest I change my mind, they hoped I might accept their job offer a year in advance of the start of the Biozentrum operations. Arber had worked out an arrangement by which I could spend the intervening year at the University of Edinburgh's Department of Molecular Biology as a Visiting Lecturer. This would be funded by a fellowship from the European Molecular Biology Organization (EMBO), a pan-European organization dedicated to research collaboration between European institutions. Furthermore, Basel agreed to make up the difference between the fellowship's stipend and the agreed Basel salary. Since Edinburgh had a major research project on restriction and modification, this arrangement was attractive to everyone.

We spent weeks examining the various job offers and alternatives. The choice was between the safe, the known (the US) and the risky, the unknown (Europe). One important person in the discussion was K.C., Ying's father. K.C. had lived and worked in Europe several times, including a stint at UNESCO in Paris, and several years at the IAEA in Vienna. He was a well-regarded radiation physicist and very cosmopolitan. To him, there was no dilemma. If we wanted to go, we should.

Our multiple trips to Europe had opened us up to the idea of living there. In the end, we felt that we would never again be this young and adventurous. We wanted the excitement of working and living in Europe. We decided that I would move to Edinburgh in January, 1971, leaving Ying-Ying to finish her thesis in Cambridge. She would join me in Edinburgh that summer and finish the final revisions on her thesis there. At the end of the year, we would make our move to Basel.

In the years since my Cambridge sojourn, I have often reflected on that period of my life. I had experienced the rigor and creativity of scientific research, fallen in love and married, and witnessed firsthand how individuals can influence issues of war and peace. It was the only period of my life when the laboratory, the beach, the dinner party, and world travel were not separate and conflicting domains. Rather, they were all part of a rich and full life.

SOMETHING OLD, SOMETHING NEW
Edinburgh - St.Tropez - Basel - College Park
1970 - 1984

My years at Harvard had launched my scientific career. The natural progression had me defining new areas of research and organizing my own research group. Since molecular biology was a totally new field with important medical and industrial applications, it involved certain distinctive characteristics.

At certain points of my life, what appeared at first to be commonplace decisions turn out to be critical in determining my future. Ordinarily, choosing a permanent position at a university may be stressful but is, nevertheless, a fairly routine matter. In my case, it represented a choice between two different cultural environments with long-term consequences on career and citizenship. The acceptance of the position at Basel also required spending a year in another European laboratory. There was the option of going to the famous Mill Hill laboratory of Molecular Biology in Cambridge University. Though attracted to Cambridge, I thought that there would be other opportunities to go there. Edinburgh was a more unusual choice in that it would introduce me to a new culture.

Edinburgh was one of the top universities in the U.K., and it introduced me to a new way of doing research. My Basel appointment was at the Biozentrum, a research institute at the university with close links to the pharmaceutical industry. It was an international institution with researchers from all over the world. I would eventually return to the US where I would be part of the National Cancer Institute (NCI), a large government research center operated under contract to a private corporation. During this time, I became increasingly involved in technology assessment and science policy. After that, I returned to the lab bench with a totally different perspective.

❧❧❧

Edinburgh: A Scottish Sojourn

The year at Edinburgh would begin the process of adaptation to life in Europe. The United Kingdom represents the union of two kingdoms, England and Scotland. Edinburgh was established in the 12th century, is the capital of Scotland and as such is its political capital and home to the Scottish Parliament and is also its major educational and cultural center. The University of Edinburgh, founded in 1583, is considered to be one of the best universities in the U.K., along with Oxford and Cambridge.

In principle, the hiatus in Edinburgh was supposed to be like a sabbatical during which I could pursue my research, work on a manuscript, and establish contacts in European science. The reality was that we were exposed to a series of new experiences for which we were not fully prepared. Right from the beginning, I had to familiarize myself with the topography of the city. The city had three major areas: the old town which dated back to the Middle Ages, the new town which had been built in the 18th century, and then the modern neighborhoods. The original university was in the city center along the Royal Mile and George Square. King's Buildings was a newer campus that included the science and engineering departments. This is where I would be based. Once I had my footing, I started to explore the culture of the place.

Scientific Cultures

Research and education in molecular biology was centered around an unusual combination of a university department, Molecular Biology, and the Molecular Genetics unit of the Medical Research Council. The former was chaired by Professor Martin Pollock, a respected researcher on the mechanisms of antibiotic resistance, and the latter was headed by Bill Hayes, an expert in genetic recombination in bacteria. The close collaboration of these two units resulted in a combination of biochemistry and bacterial genetics research that was most unusual at that time. When he moved from London's Hammersmith Hospital, Hayes had brought with him a gifted group of young geneticists among whom were Julian Gross, Marilyn Monk, Paul Broda, John Scaife, and Neil Willets. On the departmental side, biochemistry was emphasized by the work of Ken Murray on nucleic acid sequencing and Richard Ambler on proteins. Noreen Murray was a fine geneticist working on the genetics of restriction and modification.

My objective was to adapt Ken's techniques to sequence the DNA sites that were methylated or cut by the restriction endonucleases. I was also collaborating with Meselson in writing a major review on restriction and modification. I would do the necessary research for the review and write the preliminary draft. We would meet at the end of the summer to write the final manuscript.

Biochemists and geneticists differ in their approaches to science and in their lifestyles. To biochemists, it was all about working with purified enzymes and reagents in order to understand the reactions that took place in the cells. For the geneticists, the objective was to define theoretical models that could be proven indirectly through the manipulation of genes. Furthermore, though both groups had a keen appreciation for good food and fine wines, the geneticists had a much more artistic bent that found expression in the purchase and remodeling of historical homes in the New Town, the acquisition of antique furniture and china, the preparation of fancy meals, and attendance and participation in the performing arts (particularly the theater). Given the modest salary scales, this lifestyle was possible because many of them had collaborations and arrangements in the US that provided supplementary income. I and later Ying were actively encouraged to join in all of their activities.

Among American scientists, it is generally accepted that our way of doing science and research is universal. My sojourn in Edinburgh proved otherwise. The practice and priorities of science reflects the society in which it takes place. The faculty and researchers in both the department and the MRC unit were mostly English, not Scots, and many of them had been educated at Cambridge. I noticed that they were highly articulate and literate, not only in science, but also in other fields of learning. Another important difference was that, unlike in the US, science in the U.K. operated under serious financial constraints. Before one actually carried out an experiment, it was customary to think through the different ways in which this could be done before selecting the best option. And this often followed a series of discussions.

Another tradition was the daily afternoon tea. Everyone from the most junior technician to the chair or head of unit was expected to participate. Scientific exchanges were at the heart of this gathering. Going to a neighboring pub at the end of the day was another version of this. A more irksome practice was the need to re-use various consumable laboratory items that we in the US considered disposable. For example, the plastic pipette tips were saved to be washed and dried to be used again. The scintillation vials that were used to count radioactivity were saved. The counting fluid was used again while the vials were also rinsed out for further use. This was time consuming but these practices led to savings in supplies and encouraged a more thoughtful use of resources.

Another rewarding aspect of my lab experience was my close interaction with the students. In sharp contrast to the American system, the U.K. graduate students had completed their coursework by the time they began their PhD studies. They could thus concentrate on their research and on keeping abreast of the current literature. There were also the honors students who had completed their undergraduate courses and were spending a year working on a thesis project for their honors citation. I thoroughly enjoyed the scientific dialogue with students such as Bob Old and Jeremy Brockes who were doing their research with Ken Murray. The only thing that I did not do was to become an aficionado of squash as they all were.

The long months of research were frustrating in that they did not yield tangible results. Our intention had been to find the sites on the DNA that were cleaved by our restriction enzyme and, at least in theory, these should be the same or in the vicinity of the sites for methylation. Our first experimental approach was to tag with an isotope the terminus of the cleavage site. This reaction was not successful. The second possibility was to copy the DNA fragments into RNA and see whether those could then be sequenced. This was also unsuccessful. As is often the case in research, the negative results could be due to technical problems or, more seriously, to flaws in the theory. I increasingly suspected that the latter was the case and that our enzymes differed fundamentally from those studied by Ham Smith and Herb Boyer.

No Fun on the Riviera

Being invited to write a review for the Annual Review of Biochemistry is a big deal. The authors get to do a critical survey of the published work on a specific research area, present the arguments for and against the current theories, and examine some of the work in progress. Perhaps most rewarding is that they get to present their own work in the context of the field. Aside from my experimental work, I spent many hours reading papers, having lengthy discussions with Noreen Murray, and trying to integrate our own work with that done by others. The result of all this effort was a first draft. Meselson and I had agreed that we would get together in Europe at the end of the summer and take care of the revisions and rewriting of the review. Meselson and his wife, Sarah, had rented an apartment in the village of Ramatuelle in the hills above Saint Tropez in the French Riviera. So Ying and I could stay with them while we worked on the review.

Our plans called for us to work hard before heading to the continent for a holiday break and meeting up with Matt and Sarah. But we also realized that the end of August and the beginning of September was the time for the famous Edinburgh Festival. This was an annual international event of classical music, opera, dance, theater, and visual arts. It would have been sad to miss it when we were actually living in the midst of it, so we chose to go to the Festival for three days before leaving for Italy.

It was an extraordinary experience. The days were long, the weather was mild, and the streets were thronged with residents, visitors and artists. The best part is that audiences could delight at the virtuoso performances of famous artists and ensembles, and then slip into a much smaller venue and be enchanted by lute music from a young unknown musician. And all of this was just a short walk from our Manor Place flat.

Now that we were living in Europe, the exploration of its cities and nations became much simpler and more fun. Ying had been to Italy before and looked forward to guiding me through the many sights. In Rome, we absorbed the dazzling energy of street life and reveled in the glories of the ancient city. Then there was a rather nightmarish ride on a packed train to Florence. Three days passed in keen appreciation of the treasures of Renaissance Italy: the Michaelangelo statues at the Academia, the Duomo, the Piazza della Signoria, but all of this was increasingly in a daze generated by sleep deprivation. My preferred tourist sites became some of the smaller churches, dark, cool, devoid of people, where I could manage to catch moments of quiet sleep. From Florence, there was another train ride to Nice where we checked into a spacious hotel a couple of blocks from the beach and thoroughly enjoyed the sun, the sea, and the Nicoise cuisine.

Rested and refreshed, we met up with the Meselsons in Ramatuelle. The village is on the hill above St. Tropez with lovely views of the beaches and the Mediterranean below. Their flat was right next to the main square, the Place de l'Ormeau. While St. Tropez was a jet set destination with lots of activity at all hours of the day, Ramatuelle was sleepy and tranquil. Over lunch, we worked out the logistics for the next few days. The beach of Pampelonne, one of the most popular ones in St. Tropez, lay just below us. Matt and I would rise early, have a simple breakfast, head down to the beach with our papers and notes, rent one of the beach spaces, and settle down for a day's work. The ladies (Sarah was several months pregnant at the time) would join us later in the morning. We could enjoy breaks for a swim and lunch before returning to the apartment late in the afternoon. The evenings would be work free, and we would adjourn for aperitifs and dinner either in Ramatuelle or down in St. Tropez.

It did not work out exactly as planned. On the first morning, Matt and I made our way to the beach and rented a space that came equipped with lounge chairs and rattan screens on either side to provide a modicum of privacy. We sorted out the draft of the review and all of the papers and notes. As we were beginning our work, something caught Matt's eye, and he asked "Did you see that?" No, I had not noticed anything, but then I had been looking through the draft and not gazing out at the beach. But we rapidly realized that something unusual was going on. St. Tropez became famous decades earlier when it went topless. But this summer, this beach was topless and bottomless. Try as we could, it was impossible not to note the constant parade of attractive women walking along the beach in front of us. By the time Ying-Ying and Sarah joined us, we had decided that the beach was not the appropriate site for writing a scientific review.

So we had to go to Plan B. There was a café/restaurant with a shaded terrace facing the main square that seemed friendly and quiet. We planned to get there in the morning, settle down at a table with our papers, and have a simple breakfast of croissants and café au lait. We would order coffee, wine, sandwiches to justify our occupancy of that table. The owner kept an eye on us but seemed affable enough for a while. But halfway through the second morning, he came over and pointed out that he was not happy with our working there. I said that I did not understand his objection since there were other tables where customers were reading newspapers or books, playing cards, and otherwise whiling away their days. "Mais, non, ce n'est pas la meme chose." Not at all the same thing. Those people are relaxing and enjoying themselves. You are working and that gives a bad image to the café and drives away business. Please take your work elsewhere."

We were forced to fall back on the worst solution of them all, cloistering ourselves in the apartment without being able to enjoy the glorious sunshine and the picturesque images of this village on the Riviera. And though we did well in establishing the framework of the review and crafting the language of various sections, we did not finish. It would take us the rest of the year to complete the review.

A Scottish View

I had planned to find a place to live that could accommodate both of us once Ying joined me. It was complicated, and I ended up living at three different places during my Edinburgh stay. First, there was a boarding house that was within walking distance of King's Buildings. It had several advantages: a very friendly landlady, copious Scottish breakfasts, efficient central heating, and interesting boarders (many of them scientists, mathematicians from Eastern Europe). The main disadvantage was that there were no cooking facilities, so I had to eat out, and it was some distance to the center of the city.

Food has always been an important aspect of my life, and Edinburgh was to prove a particular challenge in that respect. This was particularly true in the months before Ying-Ying joined me. I had my first meal in Edinburgh when I went to the canteen with Jeremy Brockes, one of the graduate students, and discovered that the dish of the day was curried Spam with rice and chutney. Oh my God, I thought, memories of the Indian Army on the march. Not long after that, Ken Murray suggested that it might be a good idea for me to join the Faculty Club. Not only would I have a choice, a fast and inexpensive bite in their cafeteria or a more relaxed meal in the dining room, but there was also access to the wine cellar which maintained a fine selection. At that time, blue laws were in existence so that getting something to eat on Sundays was difficult. The first solution was to go down to Waverly train station where one could either eat at the station buffet or try one of the hotel restaurants along Princes St. Doing so required me to venture downtown where I might spend a fair amount for an indifferent meal.

Closer to home was King's Chinese restaurant where I could get a satisfactory Chinese meal (including various green vegetables notably absent from the Scottish diet) at a very reasonable price. It was ironic that the most practical solution was to pop down to the bakery and grocery store on Saturday afternoon to purchase rolls, cheese, and such specialties as sausage rolls, Cornish pasties, steak pies, and a variety of apples. I created a small collection of good red wines, particularly first growth Burgundies, from the University wine cellar. When I would describe my small Sunday evening picnics in my digs to my friends in New York or to Ying-Ying in Cambridge, they would not know whether to laugh or cry. Sausage rolls, a mince pie, a chunk of cheddar, a tart apple, and a bottle of Beaune or even a Gevrey Chambertin seemed a most unlikely combination. But on dark, cold rainy nights, it would certainly more than do the job.

Being well compensated, I could indulge myself in some luxuries. Ones that I will always remember include the Café Royal and the Cosmos Restaurant. The Café Royal dated back to 1826 and was in the heart of the city. Replete with stained glass, large mirrors and murals, and fine woodwork, it was a true period piece. Eating at the bar was a great pleasure: fresh oysters washed down with lager or a glass of Chablis or Muscadet. It was there that I was first introduced to haggis, the national dish of Scotland, accompanied by a shot of malt whiskey. Haggis is a sheep's stomach stuffed with minced heart, lung, liver, onions, oatmeal and spices. It is certainly an acquired taste and, for outsiders like myself, it was far easier to love the malt whiskey.

Unquestionably, the biggest (and most expensive) treat of all was to have dinner at the Cosmos Restaurant in the New Town. This was an Italian restaurant with excellent seafood (the stuffed crab was a delectable appetizer) and one could never go wrong with the veal chop. It was also very popular, and it was always wise to book a table in advance.

I was fortunate in that the MRC group loved to cook and had an adventurous palate. It all started out with a big dinner at the Gross's flat, when it came out that not only did I cook, but I could cook Chinese food. It did not take long to work out a mutually satisfactory arrangement. We would organize dinners at various homes, I would get the Chinese ingredients and cook multi-course dinners while my colleagues would provide drinks and funds – all of it making for some splendid evenings. Many in the MRC group were very much involved in the arts, particularly the theater. It was thus that I joined the Traverse Theater, which was the main source of experimental modern theater in the city. Organized as a club, the venue also allowed theatergoers to grab a bite and a pint. As would be expected, the quality of the plays was quite variable, but they made use of multi-media approaches to focus on controversial topics of the day such as feminism, homosexuality, and antiwar activism. Edinburgh was also rich with such cultural entities as the Scottish National Orchestra, the Scottish Opera, and the Lyceum Theater. All of this was readily available at affordable prices.

Soon after I arrived in Edinburgh, Bill Hayes made certain that I should be exposed to (no, captivated by) the allures of single malt whiskies. Single malt whiskies are the products of individual distilleries. Before single malts became popular in London, before they became quality tipples in Paris, and many decades before they started arriving in US shores, Edinburgh was one of the few places where one could have access to a broad range of single malts. Most of the international market was dedicated to blended whiskies (e.g., Johnny Walker) made with a selection of single malts and some grain spirits. I found malt whiskies to be an acquired taste, each with its particular quality of color, smell, taste, flavor, weight. My early experiences were far from positive: I had started out with some of the whiskies from the Lowlands such as Glenfiddich and Glenlivet that were quite distinct from such blended whiskies as Chivas Regal and Johnny Walker. It took years to learn to appreciate the special characteristics of some of my favorites such as the full bodied, amber colored Macallan (a favorite one in London), the full flavor of Highland Park from the Orkney islands, and the strongly smoky, peaty tastes of Laphroaig and Lagavulin from the island of Islay. On a cold, foggy night, Lagavulin seems less like a whisky and approaches the quality of a fine old cognac.

Eating out as a single man at good restaurants marked a cultural distinction between the US and the U.K. In the former, the single man is considered to be something of an anomaly and is often relegated to some Siberian corner of the dining room (frequently by the rest rooms). In Edinburgh, I found myself treated with deference and courtesy, and with a frequent effort to meet the requirements of an individual eater (e.g., making a starter into a main course, finding an appropriate half bottle or single glass of wine). And it would only take a few visits to a favorite restaurant to become a regular.

Another endearing quality of bachelor life was the kind way in which my friends and colleagues introduced me to their friends. They also made sure that whether at dinners or theater evenings, I would be paired off with a member of the opposite sex so that I would not feel an odd man out.

The first half of the year passed rapidly, and in July I returned to Cambridge to pack up our household belongings and bring Ying back to Edinburgh. Aside from the packing and the round of going away parties at the lab, there was one final outdoor party, held appropriately on July 4. A group of our closest friends had organized a clambake at the Chandler Hovey Park in Marblehead, Massachusetts, a quaint fishing village and home of the Boston Yacht Club. The park was located at the mouth of Marblehead Harbor, and we could look across the water at the town and the boats in the harbor. As part of New England tradition, we steamed clams, lobsters, and sweet corn, accompanied by cole slaw, white wine and beer, and finished up with chilled watermelon. Later in the evening, there was the stunning display of fireworks with music drifting across the water. It was a festive occasion, but there was a touch of sadness. We were leaving the US with its wealth of happy experiences, not knowing when or even if we would ever come back.

With the Edinburgh summer, the grey skies, drizzle, and chilly weather were gone. The sun shone and the temperature shot up into the 70s. Local residents and newspapers proclaimed that Scotland was in the midst of a heat wave. I was out of the old digs and into a spacious and fashionable flat on the West End of the New Town. Julian Gross and his wife, Marilyn, were off to the US on research leave, and we had sublet their third floor flat in Manor Place. Along with the flat came Mrs. Murray, the nanny for the Gross's son, Ben. Though we had no need for her services, the Grosses wanted us to retain her for their eventual return later that year. So Mrs. Murray became responsible for housecleaning, shopping, and perhaps most important of all, becoming our basic source on the mores of Edinburgh and Scotland. So while she was completing the writing of her thesis, Ying-Ying was learning about the rich history and traditions of the Scots. Initially, I was startled when I would walk into the apartment and hear Mrs. Murray talking to some other Scots lady. Then I realized that Ying-Ying had picked up the broad intonations and accents of the Scots.

Having a flat required a new set of logistics. In the US, these were relatively simple matters; in Edinburgh, they were anything but. To start with, there was the matter of opening a checking account. My colleagues sent me off to the local branch of the Royal Bank of Scotland. This involved a serious amount of paperwork and a long interview with the bank manager. As I was to learn, many people do not have a bank account, and the acceptability of a bank customer required establishing whether he could be considered a gentleman. This was no trivial matter as the holder of the bank account had rights to an overdraft (i.e., spending more than the funds available in the account). I found this somewhat ludicrous in that I had no desire to have an overdraft. Another business challenge arose from the fact that credit cards were not widely accepted in most stores or services. Transactions were carried out by charging purchases to your account. Since purchases were done at a variety of small shops rather than large supermarkets, it was necessary to establish accounts at all of these stores including the butcher, the fishmonger, the bookstores, and even the newsstand. As we went through this process, we realized the advantages of having the prestigious Manor Place address.

And then it was autumn, and we were suddenly faced with a crisis. The Grosses were returning early, and we would have to relinquish the apartment. Finding a furnished and equipped apartment for just a few weeks was truly difficult. Fortunately, Paul Broda and his family were making a trip to the US, and we could stay at their flat for the duration. They had two floors in a historic and elegant townhouse in Moray Place, one of the addresses in the New Town. Linda was a designer, and the house had been redone to incorporate the comforts of modern life while preserving the home's historical character. We used the guest room in the basement, but we truly loved the view from the spacious living room that looked out at the Royal Botanical Garden and further out to the Firth. That room had a floor-to-ceiling built-in bookcase where we spent many an hour climbing up the ladder to browse through their collections. In particular, we enjoyed their extensive collection of mysteries.

Living in the New Town meant that we had regular access to the neighboring shops and services, each of which had its own personality. In the process, we discovered the legendary Scottish sense of frugality. When we went to the fishmonger, we typically knew what we wanted to buy, let's say a pound of shrimp. The conversation would always begin with the fishmonger discussing the prices, e.g., the shrimp was £1.25/lb., and he would express the opinion that it was too dear at that price. But most surprising of all, he would then refuse to sell it to us because this was "not good value for money." We would usually have our way but not without a lengthy argument. How could you possibly run a business in that manner?

Just around the corner was Campbell's, the place to buy fine smoked Scottish salmon and game such as grouse or pheasant. Customers would bring the salmon that they had caught to be smoked or their grouse to be hung (till it reached the right degree of ripeness). So impressive! I also had my regular appointment with a barber on Princes St. He had pointed out that I had dandruff and it was his opinion that this was a certain sign that I was working too hard. His counsel was that I should have a regular drink of single malt and pick up golf. Since the municipal golf course was right behind the labs, I had become accustomed to the sight of golf enthusiasts walking around in the cold, grey rain. So I pointed out to him that it seemed to me that the weather limited the opportunities to go and play golf. "Ach, lad, if we allowed the rain to stop us, we would never do anything."

At the urging of my lab mates, I decided that I should purchase a sports jacket of genuine Scottish tweed. I visited one of the old established shops on George Street and asked to look at some of their jackets. As I tried them on, I observed that they were densely woven and rather heavy. In addition, the wool did not appear to have been treated, and I really smelled of sheep. When I said this to the salesman, he explained that it allowed the jacket to shed rain and that I could be outdoors (playing golf perhaps?) for long periods of time without having to worry. Furthermore, he guaranteed, "Sir, it will last you a lifetime; it will last your son's lifetime, and even perhaps your grandson's." All of which was probably true, but I also would smell of sheep. No sale.

Insofar as anyone can learn to appreciate a place and its people by working and living among them for a few months, we developed a deep affection for Edinburgh. I had always thought of Paris as the most beautiful city in the world. But Edinburgh combines the physical beauty of Arthur's Seat, the Crag, and the heights of the Castle with the Firth in the distance, the medieval architecture along the Royal Mile, and the urban Georgian grace of the New Town. Add to this the city's rich cultural life, its history, the energy of its universities, and all within the dimensions of a relatively small city. We enjoyed its warmth and hospitality, the traditional songs sung at full voice in the pubs. We paid close attention as Len Kelly instructed us as to the ways of the bagpipe and played it to our enjoyment. And it is hard for me to think of a more rare experience than watching and listening to the assembly of a thousand pipers marching by in the stadium on a crisp sunny day. These Scottish experiences are all steeped in a strong romantic tradition, but also in a deep sense of tragedy from having lost control over their fate to the conquering English. Beauty born from grief. It gives one pause.

And then before we knew it, our Edinburgh prelude to Europe was coming to an end. But not without a reminder of what a different world it had been for us. There was the final round of shopping for our new apartment in Basel during which we settled our accounts at the various shops. Ying was a favorite of our butcher who was quite saddened by our departure and who proposed that he make a large package of select cuts of Black Angus beef, and perhaps some Scottish lamb too. His offerings were certainly better than anything that we could get in Switzerland, where he also understood that meat prices were quite dear. It took quite an effort to dissuade him of that scheme. Then at the home furnishings, we ordered fancy curtains but found it difficult to get them made in time. We could not get them to understand that we were taking them to Switzerland until we resorted to saying that it was for our ski chalet there. In almost all cases, we could not just pay the balances; most insisted that we would receive a statement "at the appropriate time." This would drag out into our first couple of months in Basel.

There was the final round of parties and farewell dinners. The most memorable event was very traditional in nature. Rose Street is narrow and lies between the two major streets, George and Princes. Just about every other building is either a pub or a bar. With Jeremy at the helm, I and my friends were supposed to stop at each establishment for a pint. Being a neophyte, I would be allowed to get away with a half pint. In any event, I do not believe that we made it through more than six places, but of that I cannot even be certain since it all started dissolving into a haze after a while. A day later, we loaded our luggage into the car, and on a cold, gray morning, drove down Princes St. with a final glimpse of the Castle and Arthur's Seat. And Edinburgh took pride of place in our memories.

Basel: A Swiss Way of Life

The ten months in Edinburgh were meant to be a transition to our new life in Europe. Life in that royal city had a European sensibility but at the same time was uniquely Scottish. The University also introduced me to different ways of thinking and doing science. Basel was to be very different. And in the brief period of less than a year, I had to adapt to three different styles of doing science: American, British and Swiss.

My new position in Switzerland was at the Biozentrum in Basel. Established in 1971, the Biozentrum was a basic research institute that was part of the University of Basel. The Biozentrum represented an approach to biology that was new not only for Europe, but even for the United States. It incorporated basic research, education, and linkages with industry. The institute was interdisciplinary in nature and comprised a wide variety of departments: biochemistry, biophysical chemistry, cell biology, microbiology, structural biology, pharmacology and neurobiology. It was responsible for a new interdisciplinary undergraduate curriculum known as Biology II, an alternative to the more traditional program offered at the university. It also provided graduate programs for master's and PhD degrees, and much of the research was carried out by postdoctoral fellows. The new building and its modern equipment had been funded in part by the pharmaceutical industry, and there were collaborative projects between Biozentrum scientists and their counterparts at the research institutes in major firms such as Hoffman La Roche and Ciba-Geigy.

The Institute

The institute was housed in an elegant, airy, modern building. The laboratory suites had large windows that looked out at the city on one side and out to the city prison (where we could often watch the inmates exercising in the courtyard) and the Rhine River on the other. The laboratory suites consisted of two large laboratories, a cold room and a cold lab, and offices. The inside part of each floor contained the large pieces of common equipment used by all the groups. The corridors were wide and had white boards along the walls to promote conversations and discussions.

The professional structure of the Biozentrum was significantly different from that of the university. Traditionally, each department had one or two professors, a number of assistants that worked for the professors, and a small number of privatdozents that pursued their independent research. The Biozentrum had created project leader positions modeled after assistant professorships at US universities. The difference was that these project leaders had to go through a process of habilitation (to privatdozents), giving them the right to supervise PhD students and obtain research grants. Postdoctoral fellows were appointed as assistants.

The Biozentrum at the time had a staff of about two hundred and was organized in a manner consistent with the structure of the university while incorporating features reminiscent of US institutions. The Department of Microbiology had two full professors, as was normally the case for other academic departments. The culture of the department was defined by its two professors, who had been instrumental in the creation of the institute. Both Edouard Kellenberger and Werner Arber belonged to the generation of physicists who had transformed the biological sciences into experimental disciplines based on the principles of physics and chemistry.

The Biozentrum was an international research center that also incorporated elements of Swiss multiculturalism. When the center was created, it had been decided that its working language would be English, so the scientific and administrative staff were fluent in that language. In my department, there was a significant number of Swiss French people who had followed Kellenberger and Arber from the University of Geneva. Many of the technical staff had been recruited from the Netherlands and Sweden, and they were often multilingual in their own languages as well as English and German. In practice, we used the language that was most appropriate to the task at hand. Science was almost always in English, technical and administrative matters were commonly handled in German and, since the Genevois were a very sociable group, French was a good language for after-work hours. One of the curious experiences for me as a faculty member was to witness the ability of the Swiss to switch seamlessly from one language to another, leaving it to us foreigners to follow the details of the discussion. It was common practice to hold the faculty meetings in German (as the minutes were kept in that language). Early on, I was at a meeting and was struggling to follow Kellenberger's presentation in German. All of a sudden, I found that I could not understand a word and was plunged into a state of panic. A few minutes went by before I realized that Kellenberger was speaking in French. He had unconsciously shifted from German to French, while I tried futilely to understand a German that was not there.

Of the four Microbiology project leaders, only one was Swiss and all four of us had been hired from foreign institutions. The first group consisted of Thomas Hohn, who had come from Stanford; Jurg Rosenbusch from Harvard; and myself also from Harvard. A year later, my old friend Vincent Pirrotta came down from the Karolinska Institute in Stockholm. Hohn's work was on phages, concentrating on morphogenesis and the way in which such viruses were assembled. Rosenbusch's research focused on the structure of membrane proteins known as porins and membrane receptors. My own work tried to define the mechanism of action of both restriction and modification enzymes. The various research projects led to collaboration with other groups both within the department and with other departments (e.g., Hohn with Kellenberger's group, Rosenbusch and the Biophysics Dept., mine with Arber). Many of the postdoctoral fellows and technical staff were also foreign nationals.

The Research

While my new research group in Basel worked on the molecular mechanisms of restriction and modification enzymes, Arber expanded his work, in part looking at a new class of restriction and modification enzymes encoded by the phages P1 and P15. There were two broader scientific questions which were linked to this: Each of these enzymes contained an active site responsible for recognizing the DNA sequence and triggering its cleavage. Could mutations at this enzyme site lead to recognition of a new DNA sequence? And, while genetic exchange is advantageous, it also carries a high element of risk. So how do restriction and modification maintain an appropriate balance between genetic exchange and its suppression?

Not only had Werner's scientific interests expanded, but so had his involvement in many educational and political initiatives. Early on, he had played an important role in shaping the new Biology II curriculum for the university. I was drawn into this effort by teaching seminar courses that were analogous to the honors seminars at Edinburgh (based on the reading of original literature and oral presentations) and new short, intensive lecture/lab courses on specific topics such as nucleic acids. Switzerland is a small country, limited in its material and human resources, so maximizing its R&D required new forms of both domestic and international collaboration.

Arber was deeply involved with the Swiss Nationalfonds (the Swiss National Science Foundation is the principal government organization for basic research) and its efforts to stimulate collaboration between the various Swiss universities and research institutes. At the international level, he was heavily involved in the European Molecular Biology Organization (EMBO) which was an important source for research funding, training, and collaboration between its member countries. To a certain degree, EMBO wanted to create a critical mass in the new biology that would be equivalent to that in the US.

My research group was small. Aside from myself as project leader, there was a postdoctoral fellow, a technician, a graduate student, and usually an undergraduate student. Funding from the Basel government paid for this staffing, the capital equipment, and operating costs. In order to expand the research, I applied for additional funding from the Swiss Nationalfonds, so that eventually the group had two postdoctoral fellows, two technicians and two graduate students. Though funding was never a substantive problem, recruitment was. Through the '60s, it had been an accepted practice for PhD's from first rate US universities on both coasts to spend time in Europe, usually as postdoctoral fellows. Bill Wood and Bruce Alberts had been in Geneva, for example, and Rick Calendar at the Karolinska. As competition for academic jobs tightened up in the US, fewer Americans took the risk of going abroad. On the Swiss side, PhDs preferred to accept permanent positions, mainly in industry, and did not find a two- or three-year postdoctoral appointment to be particularly attractive. The solution was in line with the international orientation of the institute, i.e., recruiting staff from other European countries such as the Scandinavian countries, the Netherlands, and the U.K.

The research on restriction endonucleases and modification methylases had two important aspects. The conceptual one was how a protein could recognize a small specific sequence on a large DNA molecule and then act on it by either cleaving it or putting a methyl group on it. In the eyes of most, the far more important aspect was the use of the restriction enzyme to cut DNA into specific fragments that carried one or more genes. This latter characteristic made it a unique tool for what became known as genetic engineering, the insertion of foreign gene(s) into any cell.

As always in research, our story turned out to be more complex. The enzyme that we had focused on was purified from E. coli K and we had named it EcoK. It then became evident that there were three classes of restriction enzymes: I, II, and III.

EcoK belonged to Type I, which was the most complicated in that it was composed of three different protein subunits and was able to either cleave the DNA or modify it. It also required two small chemical compounds, ATP (an energy compound) and AdoMet (a methyl donor).

Understanding the mechanism of action of EcoK required interdisciplinary collaboration and the development of new tools. Arber's group studied the genetics of several restriction and modification systems. Kellenberger's group was exploring the use of electron microscopy for the study of biological structures. Mutant strains obtained from Arber enabled us to isolate defective EcoK enzymes which allowed us to study the individual steps in the reaction. The activity consists of four separate stages: enzyme activation by binding AdoMet, recognition of the DNA sK site, enzyme action (either methylation if the DNA was partly modified or cleavage if it was totally unmodified), and loss of nuclease activity following DNA cleavage.

The sK DNA site can exist in three different configurations: unmodified (both DNA strands are unmethylated), modified (both DNA strands are methylated) and heteroduplex (one strand methylated, one strand unmethylated). In each case, the EcoK enzyme is triggered in a different way: on unmodified DNA, it cleaves DNA at a site distal to the sK site; if modified, it releases from the DNA; if heteroduplex, it methylates the unmethylated DNA strand. Much of what we learned was dependent on new technologies:

- Gel electrophoresis allowed us to separate DNA fragments according to their size. It was mystifying in that Type II enzymes generated different size fragments, while Type I enzymes resulted in a mixture of undefined sizes.

- Electron microscopy of enzyme-DNA complexes allowed us to map the location of the sK sites.

- Affinity chromatography allowed for efficient purification of the various enzymes.

My graduate student, Jakob Reiser, and I had worked on a different enzyme from the phage P15. Originally it was believed to be a Type I enzyme given its requirement for AdoMet and ATP and its ability to catalyze both DNA cleavage and methylation. Our detailed experiments showed that EcoP15 belonged to a new class of enzymes that we named Type III. While the enzyme recognized a specific sequence, it actually cleaved the DNA 25-26 bases away from it.

During the early years, much of our excitement was fueled by our interactions with other research groups which shared fundamental interests, methods, and reagents, as well as common interests both in and out of the laboratory. Christine Brack pioneered in the electron microscopy of protein-DNA complexes. Vincenzo Pirrotta was an old friend and colleague from the Harvard days. Initially, he worked on the binding of the lambda repressor to different sites in the operator that switches transcription from the PR promoter (and therefore lytic growth) to the Prm promoter. Later on, Vincent began to shift his work toward the fruit fly Drosophila, and he collaborated with Paul Schedl and Spyros Artavanis in the Cell Biology Dept. Vincent was the first one to set up the DNA sequencing system of Maxam and Gilbert and worked with Susumu Tonegawa at the Basel Institute of Immunology to determine the sequence of the junction between the constant and variable regions of the immunoglobulin gene. This was a major breakthrough that allowed DNA to be sequenced.

Aside from the intense lab work, we also greatly enjoyed good food and wine, cooking, hiking in the neighboring mountains. Spyros's wife, Popi, and his little daughter, Katerina, were good company to Ying and our daughter, Nikki. And this also gave Paul and Spyros the opportunity to borrow and read Nikki's classic comic books of TinTin.

Arber's Work in Education and International Collaboration

I had worked with Meselson and Arber for years and had found them to be different in their attitudes and temperaments. With time I have noticed certain similarities and know that both of them influenced me significantly in my own career. While both men were accomplished scientists, by the time I joined Meselson at Harvard, he was already deeply involved in government policy particularly as related to arms control. He combined a keen eye for detail and methodology with creative insights into biological processes.

Meselson had always encouraged me to become familiar with policy issues as related to chemical and biological warfare. Though intellectually challenging, at that point in my career there was little that I could do in such fields. The situation was different in Basel since teaching responsibilities, conferences, and involvement in EMBO projects including international workshops provided me with practical experience in Arber's activities outside of the lab.

Arber brought to his research a more methodical and measured approach. Having enjoyed a very rapid rise in his academic career in Switzerland culminating in his professorship in Basel, Arber now had the opportunity to explore new interests. His first initiatives related to undergraduate education particularly as related to the creation of the new Biology II curriculum which incorporated small group seminars, block courses (intensive lecture/lab courses) in specific subjects, and scientific workshops. Along with that, he became involved in issues of science policy and funding within the Swiss Nationalfonds. Arber, along with certain other prominent Swiss researchers, realized that a small country like Switzerland was limited in its research capabilities and therefore needed to establish collaborative agreements at the international level. Thus, he became involved with EMBO and initiatives within the EU. Such efforts were consistent with his scientific career and less tied to politics than Meselson's. Though

I had always been interested in policy, it was not the right time or place to pursue that interest. I stuck with Arber for the time being.

Counting Down

As we got into 1976, I was coming to the end of my five-year appointment. There were four of us project leaders, and we knew that it was likely that only one of us would be promoted to a professorship. I had another consideration. Even if we stayed in Switzerland, we were very unlikely to get Swiss citizenship and we would, for all practical purposes, continue to be stateless. So it was time for us to return to the United States.

During this period, Paul Berg (Stanford) came to give a seminar. He also advised me to return to the US and suggested that I look into openings at Princeton where I knew Bruce Alberts and Abe Worcel. So began the tedious and lengthy process of contacting colleagues and friends and examining different job possibilities. I found out that Michael Yarmolinsky, who was head of a lab at the Pasteur Institute in Paris, was moving back to a position at the National Cancer Institute in Maryland and was looking for people for his new group.

Our last few months in Switzerland went by in a blur of all-consuming activities. First was the question of a new position, flying to Paris for long discussions with Yarmolinsky and Stuart Austin (whom I knew from Edinburgh), who was joining the NCI group. These conversations were made far easier in that we all shared a common experience of working in Europe and were now intent on returning to the States. Then I flew to Washington to visit the new NCI facility in Frederick for interviews and discussions with Michael Hanna, the director, and his newly hired section heads. The offer from the NCI came very rapidly with a well-defined package that included the financing of my group. I was expeditiously appointed to the position of group leader in Yarmolinsky's section with the understanding that if all worked out I would be promoted to section head with no undue delay.

We began the laborious preparations for our move. For the colleagues in the Biozentrum, it was natural that researchers came and went in pursuit of their career objectives. But for our other friends and acquaintances in Basel, it was altogether a different matter. Because the quality of life in Switzerland is high and appears unchanging and stable, it was somewhat unimaginable to our friends in the community that we were leaving. Then it was time to go, stopping in Paris for a week of dining and shopping. This farewell to Europe had a modernist flavor as we found the former food markets at Les Halles now converted into a high-end shopping mall, and the newest museum being the rather factory-looking Musee Pompidou. Perhaps this was symbolic of our return to the US.

Home to a New World

When I left for Europe I had lived in the US for almost sixteen years, longer than I had lived anywhere. These had been my formative years, and it had been a transient life as an undergraduate, a graduate student, and a postdoctoral fellow. Going back to the US made us feel that we were finally going home. But the reality was that we were going to an America that we did not really know.

For one thing, we had always lived in cities. Now we'd be making a transition into suburban living where the lifestyle felt more foreign than Scotland or Switzerland. Also, Ying-Ying's work had also been at universities, and now she would join one of the ubiquitous consulting firms that characterize the Washington area.

My scientific career had also always been in universities. In contrast, my new job was in one of the world's largest biomedical research institutes with the mission of finding the causes and cures for cancer.

Universities and research facilities are two different universes. Universities carry out both research and teaching and, while most of the funding comes from external sources, many of the decisions are taken by academic committees. The government institutes are funded as a whole solely to do research, and they are organized in a hierarchical fashion.

The Frederick Cancer Center was a hybrid institution owned by the government but operated under contract to Litton, a large defense corporation. It combined academic politics, corporate interests, and the intrigues associated with large government contracts.

The War on Cancer

My new position was as a senior scientist and group leader at a new research center of the National Cancer Institute, one of the National Institutes of Health located in Bethesda, a suburb of Washington. However, this new cancer research center was located in rural Frederick, Maryland, some forty-eight miles from the center of power in Washington.

The creation of a cancer center was a major challenge involving congressional legislation, budgeting, award of contracts, construction, and staffing. While the administration and the Congress were willing to fund the new war on cancer, Congress was unwilling to construct the new research facilities nor create about 1,000 new government positions. The political solution was to make the center a government owned, corporate operated facility in which the contractor, Litton Bionetics, was paid all costs and a guaranteed profit. Litton Bionetics was part of Litton Industries, a major defense contractor. In effect, almost all of us at the Frederick facility were Litton employees, eliminating the need for new government positions.

Initially there were three major research programs: Basic Research, Chemical Carcinogenesis, and Viral Carcinogenesis, as well as a major fermentation/production facility and an animal facility. Each research program had a director who reported to the head of one of the NCI's intramural divisions. Operationally, the center was run by a general manager, Robert Stevenson, who was a Litton executive. My program was the Cancer Biology Program, directed by Michael Hanna and divided into several sections: Molecular Genetics (Michael Yarmolinksy), Virology (Jim Ihle), Immunology (Jack Marchalonis), Metastasis (Josh Fidler), and UV carcinogenesis (Margaret Kripke). Hanna also had his own small research group that worked on cancer vaccines.

The Cancer Biology Program embodied two different scientific and social cultures. All sections except Molecular Genetics focused on cancer and made extensive use of animal or human models. Jim Ihle's group was investigating the mechanism by which chronic viral infection could lead to cancer, while Margaret Kripke's group studied how ultraviolet radiation (in possible combination with certain chemicals) could lead to skin cancer. Jack Marchalonis's group tried to understand the way in which an immune response could block the proliferation of cancer cells. One of the most fascinating problems was that of metastasis, which was under study by the Fidler group. An initial tumor is localized at a primary site, but the cancer cells can migrate to other locations in a process known as metastasis. The factors that allowed cancer cells to metastasize were poorly understood. The research that was most clinically relevant was Michael Hanna's development of cancer vaccines. His experiments involved the removal of solid colon tumors which were then made into cellular preparations that were used as vaccines against the homologous tumors. Such preparations were tested in clinical trials with human patients.

While these groups worked on animal systems, Michael Yarmolinsky's section studied basic biological processes such as replication, recombination, and control of viral infection using bacteria and their viruses as their experimental systems. In particular, Yarmolinsky looked at the temperate virus P1 and the ways in which it could transfer genes from one host to another. Mutants were used to dissect the steps involved in that recombinational process. My Nucleic Acids group was part of Yarmolinsky's section but was focused on the molecular biology of restriction and modification and the study of IS2 elements.

Many bacterial strains modify their DNA, thus identifying the strain in which the DNA has been replicated. These strains are also able to restrict (destroy) DNAs that do not carry the appropriate modification. Transposable genetic elements are flanked by two IS2 elements that enable them to be moved from one chromosome to another. I was particularly interested in the binding and reactions of the restriction enzymes on the DNA. We were able to visualize the different types of complexes by using electron microscopy carried out by Dan Hamilton and Diane Plentovich in my group, and we had been fortunate in being able to bring in Christine Brack from Basel for a few weeks to set up the electron microscopy techniques for working with DNA-protein complexes. Jean Burkhardt had also come over from Zurich to work as a postdoctoral fellow in my lab. Rich Musso was a senior scientist in my group working on the IS2 elements.

The Dynamics of Biological Research

The years at Frederick coincided with the explosive growth of biological research and the emergence of the new biotechnology industry. While pursuing our own research, we were also developing a series of complex relationships with other scientific organizations such as the Army, the NCI, Litton Bionetics, and universities.

From the outset, there were tensions between the Frederick contract operation and the parent NCI. One trivial way in which this surfaced was the naming of the Frederick Center, since the

NCI wanted it to be evident that the latter was an appendage of the NCI. The first name was the Frederick Cancer Research Center, but after a few years that was changed to the NCI Frederick Cancer Research Facility, and lo, many years later, it was back to the NCI Cancer Research Center. It was all political. If the Frederick Center was a facility, it would be under contract and decisions on projects, priorities, staff would be made at the NCI in Washington. If the Center was self-standing, it would be more independent. The cold reality centered on the autonomy of the center and its access to resources. The establishment of a new center provided a rare opportunity for an interdisciplinary approach to cancer that studied how chemicals, radiation, and viruses could transform normal cells into cancer cells. At the same time, there was research into new modalities for clinical treatment, e.g. vaccines and immunomodulators.

The fact that Frederick had access to new facilities, equipment, and staff gave it a significant advantage over its counterparts on the Bethesda campus. On the other hand, NCI staff were federal employees who enjoyed job tenure and program stability. The geneticists and molecular biologists amongst us shared common research interests and methodologies with our NCI colleagues. It was therefore natural that we developed a weekly research seminar (called the lambda lunches) that alternated between Bethesda and Frederick. There was a rich research collaboration between our groups.

The intramural programs in Bethesda had not been subject to regular scientific review such as that required by university labs receiving NIH grants. An important step taken by Michael Hanna in the Basic Research Program was the establishment of a Scientific Advisory Committee composed of well-known academic researchers and charged with a regular review of our research every three years. The chairs of these review committees were such prominent scientists as Sherman Weissman (Yale Medical School) and Jim Watson (Cold Spring Harbor Labs). To us, the reviews were challenging, stressful, and time consuming but, for the most part, we came off with high marks, and it was the general opinion of the reviewers that the quality of the research was equal to that of the best university laboratories. They were surprisingly supportive of the non-competitive nature of our funding.

A Changing of the Guard in Frederick

During the period from 1977 to 1985, FCRF went through a period of exponential growth. Much of it was due to a complex interaction involving Michael Hanna, director of the Basic Research Program, and Vincent DeVita, the director of the NCI, along with the various scientific advisory committees and firms that were contracted to run FCRF. Up to this point, the accepted treatments for cancer were surgery and radiation, the former involving the removal of cancerous tissue while the latter was used to kill the tumor. Both lacked specificity and had significant side effects. This began to change with experimentation in chemotherapy that used drugs to block the growth of tumor cells. At the same time, there was growing interest in the genetics and biology of cancer cells. The developing model for cancer research was one for interdisciplinary research which would range all the way from molecular studies on DNA replication and transcription to clinical studies on patients using vaccines and biological modifiers. This approach received wide support from DeVita and the scientific committees who saw FCRF as a model for this new type of cancer research. The government-owned, corporation-operated management approach speeded up the construction of new facilities and the recruitment of scientific staff.

Michael Hanna was promoted from director of Cancer Biology to director for all of FCRF. Two new senior scientists were recruited, Mark Pearson and Thomas Silhavy. Pearson's research focused on the transfer of mammalian genes into animal cells, while Silhavy worked on cell membrane systems. Yarmolinsky's

Molecular Genetics section was reorganized, and I got my own Nucleic Acids Section. Nat Sternberg got his own group that worked on the molecular genetics of lambda and P1.

The creation of a Nucleic Acids Research Section gave me the opportunity to recruit some highly qualified young scientists such as Bob Deich from Hamilton Smith's lab and Bob Grafstrom from Larry Grossman's lab. Each of them was able to develop his own research group. Deich worked on the mechanism of genetic transformation in Hemophilus. Bob Grafstrom set up research on the synchrony between DNA replication and DNA methylation using a cell free system. Once it reached its steady state, my section of twelve people was fairly cohesive both in its scientific objectives (i.e., the interactions between specific proteins and DNA sequences) and its methodologies. We were also socially compatible, with frequent parties, dinners, and a regular Friday gathering where we shared our experiences of the past week over beers.

Managing Science

The years at Frederick represented a learning process that combined scientific direction and increasing management responsibilities. In my earlier positions I had directed a research project with the members of my group working on different aspects of it. Here, each scientist defined and pursued his or her own specific project, though there was extensive collaboration within the section, particularly as related to the methods used and the resources available. Though I maintained my own projects, more and more of my time was spent on administrative responsibilities. There was inevitably a tension between the scientists as they competed for resources (usually at the time of reviews) and for raises and promotions. FCRF was a curious hybrid in that it did not have the defined structure of academia leading to a tenured position nor the civil service framework of the NCI. Here the personal objective was to focus on resources and promotion hoping eventually to become an independent group leader or section head. This was not a simple process since it required successful review by the external scientific committee and then the approval of the program director and, finally, of Michael Hanna as center director. The management styles of section heads depended on their temperaments. There were those like Yarmolinsky, Sternberg, and Ihle who were more laissez-faire, while I and Mark Pearson had an ongoing dialogue about how to better lead our sections. But the most important management experience was what I learned from my interactions and observations with Michael Hanna.

Hanna was young, aggressive, and a quick learner. Even though he had unquestioned authority over us, in age and experience he was quite close to us, his section heads. Scientifically, the work on whole animals and disease models was closer to his own interests in pathology, but he also realized that genetics and molecular biology were essential in understanding the biology of cancer cells. During these years, Hanna had taken the trouble to educate me in the complexities of management. And one of the points he had driven home was that the three fundamentals for success in running a group were staffing, space, and money. Of those, the most difficult problems were associated with personnel. He kept a close eye on his staff, as evidenced by his penchant for wandering through the labs at all hours, initiating conversations with whoever was around, and having an uncanny knowledge of the bonds and tensions between different individuals.

Early during my tenure at Frederick, I had gone into my lab on a Saturday morning to make up some reagents and work on some bacterial strains. I was rather despondent, in part, because it was taking a lot of time and work to get my lab up and running. There was lab remodeling, purchasing of equipment and reagents, recruitment of staff, and standardization of procedures. At the same time, there was the problem of cultural reentry: suburban Washington was a totally different world from Switzerland, and both wife and daughter were also having to adapt. Just a few days earlier I had been contacted regarding a professorship that had opened up in Geneva. Feeling out of sorts, I was sorely tempted to return to the cozy and comfortable environment that I was familiar with. But then again, I was not sure that we wanted to put ourselves through the whole process of moving the household again. I was startled when Hanna walked in, pulled up a stool, and sat down to talk.

He asked how things were progressing in the lab, and then commented that I did not seem happy. I tried to give a positive spin to my settling in when he brought up the fact that there was talk that I might be thinking of going back to Switzerland. He had done a great deal to recruit me to Frederick and I should tell him what I was unhappy with, and he promised to do everything possible to take care of those problems. I was totally speechless and struggled to assure him that I had no serious complaints nor any desire to give up on Frederick. This was the first (but not the last) time that I witnessed his familiarity with lab gossip and the effective use of it to deal with a wide variety of problems.

Once, at a meeting in his office, he remarked casually whether I knew that one of my scientists (who was married) was having an affair with a technician. Taken by surprise, I replied that I did not know and, in any case, it was none of my business. He smiled. No, your job is to know everything that goes on. In the end, watching, knowing, acting were the elements of his management style. But there was also an element of ruthlessness. When a senior scientist became rather fixated in his research and ended up in intense disputes with his postdoc and technician, I was called to his office and told to take immediate action and bring it to an end. "Bob, it is your section, and your decision, but if it was up to me, I would get rid of all of them."

The Frederick Center had reached a high degree of productivity due to a gifted scientific staff and the abundance of resources which resulted in first class facilities. This state of abundance was unlikely to last, so we made an effort to increase the level of scientific collaboration both within and outside of our campus. Within the Cancer Biology Program, there was a lively program of research and literature seminars which helped to bring together the sections. The molecular/genetic sections also had the regular lambda seminars with our counterparts at NIH. At the beginning, the Center maintained a conference center called Peace and Plenty, converted from a gentleman's farm, with guest rooms and a dining facility. This historical house, surrounded by the rolling Maryland countryside and endowed with a fine wine cellar (selected by Bob), was the site of regular research seminars that brought together the three different programs at the Center.

An End to Innocence

I could not have foreseen that this period in Frederick would mark major changes in my life, my career, my interests, and my personal life, and that eight years after returning from Switzerland, I would be heading back to Europe entrusted with a challenging official project.

My own research had focused on the role of DNA methylation in bacteria and their viruses. Research in a number of laboratories had shown that DNA methylation was related to restriction of DNA when it is moved between different strains of bacteria and to a proofreading system that corrects for errors in DNA replication. What remained a major mystery was the role of DNA methylation in eukaryotic cells (cells from higher organisms). There was extensive DNA methylation there, but it did not appear to occur at specific DNA sequences as was the case in bacteria.

We began our studies on mouse cells but faced a major obstacle: we lacked a knowledge of the genetics of DNA methylation (unlike the situation in bacteria). Our approach was to try to characterize the mouse enzyme(s) responsible for DNA methylation. We soon found out that purification of the activity rapidly resulted in its inactivation. The DNA methylase activity was associated with the nuclear matrix, the insoluble complex that is composed of the chromosome and its associated proteins. A great deal of our knowledge of modern biochemistry is based on soluble enzymes. On the other hand, there is very little known about insoluble enzymes. Our studies indicated that this DNA methylation appeared to be involved in the assembly of the nucleosomes that make up the chromosome. At that time, we did not have the techniques that would allow us to dissociate the nuclear matrix and then reassemble it in such a way that would enable us to dissect the relationship between DNA replication, DNA methylation, and chromosomal assembly.

As Bob Grafstrom and Dan Hamilton increased their efforts on the DNA methylation project, I struggled to spend time in the laboratory. More and more time was spent on administrative matters, writing papers, and keeping up with the other projects in my section. As Hanna had said time and again, personnel matters consume an inordinate amount of time. Two problems emerged between my scientists and postdocs/technicians that worked for them. In one case, a senior scientist became more and more isolated to the degree that none of his subordinates wanted to work with him. Dealing with this was painful, but the second one turned out to be even more difficult. The group working on genetic transformation appeared to have made significant progress in characterizing the structures that took up DNA from the surrounding environment. The results could not be reproduced and one of the postdocs informed me that she suspected that the results had been faked. At the time, data falsification was unheard of, and there were no accepted procedures for investigating suspicious data. By this time, Mark Pearson was director of the program. I obtained the data and rigorously examined all of it, followed by a review carried out by Pearson. Since the scientist involved had worked previously for my friend, Hamilton Smith, I had the latter also review the information. The conclusion of all of us was that the initial results were an artifact and that there was no evidence of the fabrication of the data. However, this incident was to have very unpleasant consequences.

At the same time, life was becoming more and more fragmented. Ying-Ying was busier than ever with her consulting practice, and her business travel was increasing. Nikki had a full life with her schoolwork, her extracurricular activities which included ballet, and her own circle of friends. Eventually, we decided that she would get a better education by enrolling in a newly established International Baccaleurate high school program established in a neighboring town. One positive outcome was that I established good friendships with the fathers of two of Nikki's friends. Brock Smith was a construction engineer at one of the massive building projects at NIH, and Ed Woods, a former Navy carrier pilot who was a surgeon at the Naval Medical Center. The three of us would take the kids for jaunts such as Halloween trick-or-treating and reward ourselves with martinis and cigars. They were interesting people and truly good company.

Our family had always made a practice of taking a two-week vacation during the summer. But now, Ying could come for only part of the time, and it finally reached a point where Nikki and I would go to Calella, our favorite Spanish village, without Ying.

As we moved into the 1980s, life became increasingly turbulent. I had gotten closer to the program directors and worked with Michael Hanna on various center-wide initiatives. There were growing tensions between the NCI (particularly at the level of the director) and the Frederick contract operation (as headed by Hanna). The first major development was when the Frederick contract was divided into three separate contracts, with Litton retaining only the Cancer Biology Program. Then rather than having the scientific reviews follow a 3-year cycle, the reviews took place almost every year, and there was a trend to change the research directions and move towards the study of oncogenes. There were growing rumors that various sections would be dissolved and replaced by new ones. Section heads and senior scientists began to explore other job opportunities. Mark Pearson was one of the most active in the process, negotiating with Dupont regarding the creation of a large new drug research program. Dupont hired a group of Frederick scientists to its research center in Wilmington, Delaware. I was getting concerned but did not have any great enthusiasm to move to Dupont. I thought a lot about returning to university life, but did not want to have to relocate my family away from the Washington area.

An appropriate opportunity turned up at the University of Maryland under the leadership of Rita Colwell, who had decided to set up a Maryland Biotechnology Institute (MBI) composed of five separate centers. The positions would involve dual appointments to one of the MBI centers and a faculty position in one of the departments at the University of Maryland, College Park. While the biology departments at UMCP were not particularly distinguished, there was a major commitment by its president and the state to launch an ambitious new effort to make UMCP a leader in biological research and education. I accepted the professorship.

CHANGING COURSE: A DIPLOMATIC LEGACY

College Park - France - Germany - Italy Netherlands - Norway - Finland - Denmark Sweden - Spain - Switzerland - United Kingdom 1984 - 1986

As I was preparing to return to academia, I received a phone call that would transform my life. Dr. Alfred Hellman at the National Cancer Institute (NCI) was setting up a project at the International Trade Administration (US Department of Commerce). Its objective was to study the competitive advantage of the US biotechnology industry over its major rivals in Western Europe and Asia.

Science had always been both an intellectual pursuit and a practical necessity. Yet both my father and grandfather had been career diplomats, and I had grown up in a diplomatic world. I would probably have followed them into a diplomatic career. But with China now under Communist rule, both my parents and my professors had advised me to pursue a scientific career, first in chemistry and then molecular biology. I had found science to be thoroughly exciting. Now fate presented me with the opportunity to enter the world of diplomacy and science policy, and to learn a new body of knowledge and skills.

I had been highly recommended to Dr. Hellman, and we arranged for a meeting with two senior officials at the ITA and a member of the White House staff. We had a lengthy discussion regarding my research career in the US and Europe, my familiarity with the nascent biotechnology industry, and my ideas on how to carry a biotechnology assessment in Western Europe. The project would involve a temporary appointment in the Foreign Service and a posting to a US Embassy in Europe. I would report directly to Deputy Assistant Secretary Mike Kelley in Washington.

All of a sudden, I would be able to explore my interests in international affairs. It was risky in that it led me to a different world. Despite a strong family background, I had no experience in the intricacies of diplomacy. I'd also never been responsible for an international project of a temporary nature and unknown future. But I did have familiarity with taking risks and making choices. An immediate decision needed to be made: Should I resign the professorship I had just accepted or should I negotiate an arrangement with the university? Mike Kelley advised me not to worry about it, he would take care of it. Kelley contacted John Toll, president of the University of Maryland at College Park, requesting that I be put on leave so as to carry out this technology assessment for the International Trade Administration. The university agreed.

My assignment would begin early in 1985 and I would return to campus in the fall semester of 1986. This was an important lesson for the future: When powerful people want things done, things get done.

⁂

The Training of a Foreign Service Officer

In the months between the end of 1984 and the beginning of 1985, my life moved in dual tracks. There was the drudgery of winding down the activities of my NCI research section and helping my people find new jobs. Then there were the necessary preparations for my Foreign Service assignment, the training, and an endless wait for the security clearance.

A new Foreign Service officer starts out by taking the five-week A-100 Introductory Training Class. Carrying my documents, I was shuttled across to the Foreign Service Institute for my first class. As I and some hundred other trainees crowded into the conference room, I heard the instructor on stage call out, "Oh my God, look who just walked in." Everyone assumed it was some VIP such as George Schultz (the Secretary of State). No, no such luck, it was just my humble self. But the instructor was Glenn Munro, a senior diplomat and a former classmate of mine from Antioch. He had never expected to see me there, nor had I imagined that he would be one of my instructors. We had a good laugh about that.

The five weeks went quickly. I moved on to the Western Europe area studies course. Though the participating group was smaller, it was much more diverse, including both entering and senior career officers who were being transferred to new European assignments. Over the years I had become well read in European literature, history, and politics and had traveled extensively in the region. This had been scarcely relevant to my scientific research, but suddenly it proved invaluable. I did very well in my classes and in my interactions with my instructors.

I had chosen to undergo additional language training in German and had been assigned a tutor. She and I fashioned a program where I read articles from newspapers and journals on politics and international affairs and then held conversations and discussions. I also did translations of these materials.

I was given three choices for my embassy posting: London,

Paris, or Brussels. Though I was tempted by the idea of serving in Paris, the decision was self-evident. The London Embassy was the largest US mission at the time and a hub for European operations. It could therefore provide the necessary logistical support for this European project. I would have a personal assistant that would staff my office when I was on travel and help with the research and preparation of reports. Robert Fujimura, an Oak Ridge scientist of Japanese descent, was sent to the US Embassy in Tokyo to carry out a parallel study on biotechnology in Japan. Last but not least, the London assignment would provide a transition to a new career.

Security Matters

There had been quite a few aircraft hijackings and terrorist attacks on US diplomats. One of my most absorbing and disturbing courses had to do with security and preventive measures against terrorist attacks, something that most of us had never encountered. Presentations and discussions were provided by security officers and by US diplomats that had been involved in an incident. There were briefings as to the groups responsible for anti-American activities and their areas of operations. Then there were practical recommendations regarding ways to detect surveillance and shadowing, carry out avoidance and evasion, and finally work out what to do in the case of kidnapping or capture. As to the latter, there was a somber presentation by one of the US diplomats held captive by the Iranians for 444 days in the US Embassy in Tehran. He emphasized the importance of planning out how to act in such situations and discussing procedures with his wife so that when something happened, he could at least be secure in the knowledge of what his family would be doing. These security instructions were to be repeated by the Regional Security Officer and again by a Metropolitan Police officer at the embassy in London. My own reactions alternated between black humor and an increased sensitivity to my surroundings. This instruction would prove helpful in the field.

Project Planning

The preparations for the project accelerated. An important step was for Fujimura and me to familiarize ourselves with the US biotechnology companies. The two of us, along with Al Hellman, visited some thirty firms located around Boston and San Francisco. Even at its birth, biotech was a highly diverse industry. Some companies were major multinationals such as Dupont, but the majority were small, new companies such as Genentech, DNAX, Biogen. While many of them focused on the development of new drugs, there were others like Centocor and Biotechnology Research Laboratories that created new diagnostics and reagents, and Applied Biosystems that manufactured equipment for the sequencing of proteins and DNA. It was striking to see the major differences between the research labs in institutes and universities and these high tech firms that pursued highly sophisticated research and their applications while searching for appropriate business models to make them profitable.

For our next step, Hellman and I made a one-week trip to London to set up our project at the US Embassy. This was complicated in that I was being sent out from Washington to work at the Embassy as a Foreign Service officer. We expected that I and my assistant would receive office space and logistical support in the Commercial Section. The Commercial Counselor was not particularly supportive and instead got us office space at the US Naval Headquarters (across the street from the Embassy). This was awkward since my European contacts were likely to interpret this as meaning that this was an intelligence project. Fortunately, Robert Stella, the science counselor, became interested in technology assessment and competitiveness. Since he had a large suite of offices, he invited me to work out of the science office which gave our project a much more technological and academic character. Aside from the many meetings and administrative discussions, Hellman and I were able to take advantage of London's lively cultural life, enjoying some fine meals, catching some shows, and taking long walks through the city.

I was fortunate that my budget provided for a personal assistant. This was invaluable since my mission required continuous travel throughout Western Europe and extensive research using U.K. sources. We were not certain of the appropriate background for the P.A. and would need to get him or her security clearance to work at the Embassy. I recruited Becky Roberts, who had been an Air Force captain and also a nutritionist. Her husband was responsible for embassy communications not only in London, but also at other missions in Europe. Becky combined sharp organizational skills with a sense of diplomacy that was useful in dealing with VIP's. She was also friendly and had a good sense of humor. The objectives of this biotechnology program:

- Determine the government policies in support of biotechnology
- Identify the principal research laboratories and their activities
- Identify the principal companies involved in biotechnology and its applications
- Study the various mechanisms for technology transfer from the research laboratories to the industrial sector.

Technology assessment was totally new to Commerce and the embassies, so we had to establish a procedure that would enable us to obtain documents, do interviews with key officials and scientists, prepare cables and reports, and carry out briefings. For example, for the study of biotechnology in Switzerland, there would be preliminary research on the biotechnology activities in the country, and key individuals and organizations would be identified. We would connect with personal contacts, ask for assistance from the embassy in Switzerland, and secure approval from the US London Embassy. Washington would issue the appropriate travel orders assigning me to temporary duty at the US Embassy in Bern.

My approach was to gather as much background information about the individuals and organizations that I was visiting. Our conversations would involve:

- Describing the project in order to understand how new knowledge leads to economic growth.
- Sharing of what I had learned both in the US and Europe, specifically what worked and what did not work.
- Project design and the importance of diversity (science, political, racial/cultural identity) in selection of the researchers. I was an example of this approach.

That our reports would be shared with the various European governments was important. After the visits were completed, a reporting cable would be sent to Washington with copies to the embassies in London and in Bern. We would prepare and send a detailed country report to the US Embassy in Bern for comments and review. At last, the Department of Commerce in Washington would approve and release the final report and, as a courtesy, make copies available to the Swiss authorities.

A Different Way of Life

Those seventeen months marked a major turning point in my life, a retrofit that turned me from a research scientist and administrator into an analyst. My job was to understand how science and technology could be used as a major driver for economic development and societal change. The multinational nature of the project acquainted me with most of the countries in Western Europe and gave me an opportunity to use my knowledge of Spanish, French, and German. I did not quite realize then that this was the beginning stage of globalization, a process that would accelerate over the following years. I feel very lucky that at the age of 47, I was able to engage in such a transformative experience, both in terms of mastering a variety of subjects and developing new skills in an international context.

What was not evident was how any of this would be relevant to my new position at the University of Maryland or in identifying new professional opportunities elsewhere. There was also the sweet irony that, as a Chinese, I had acted as a representative of the United States in a variety of countries but that, in so doing, I first had to internalize my identity as an American.

Many of my experiences altered my perception of the world around me. One serious concern was the dangerous security situation at the time due to the collaboration between Palestinian terrorists and such European groups as the Red Brigades and the Baader-Meinhof gang. A number of US diplomats had been kidnapped or assassinated. Diplomats going overseas were taught to be alert at all times, to detect enemy surveillance, and to practice avoidance tactics. Under the most extreme circumstances, we were also conditioned to make the split second decision on fight or flight ... or surrender.

Well into my project, I had planned a trip to Italy, home to several top laboratories and major multinational corporations. My personal assistant, the American embassies in London and Rome, and the Italian Ministry of Science and Technology had all invested many weeks in working out the detailed schedule. At the last minute, the State Department declared a high alert and ordered the cancellation of any but the most essential travel in Europe, particularly in Italy. The country was lax in security, and several Palestinian hit teams had been reported there. I decided to proceed with the Italian trip anyway.

Prior to leaving London, I was briefed by the Regional Security Officer. Since it could be assumed that the American Embassy in Rome was under observation, visits to the US diplomats coordinating my meetings were to be kept to an absolute minimum. Normally, arrangements were made for us to stay at good, well known hotels such as the Hilton or the Meridien. This time I was booked into the Hotel Adriano, a nondescript middle-class hotel that catered mainly to Italians and Europeans. The hotel had an ideal location close to the Via Veneto, one of Rome's principal avenues. As requested, my room was on an upper floor. I made sure that it did not have any windows opening out onto a fire escape and that I had easy access to more than one exit. Unless on visits or meetings, I was to stay in the hotel.

The next morning, I walked to the American Embassy, which was cordoned off by the carabinieri, the Italian paramilitary police force. Inside the Embassy, security was provided by Marine guards. It was an indicator of the high level of security that the Marines were not wearing their usual dress uniforms but were clad in battle fatigues and bulletproof vests and carrying M16s.

I had just finished my meeting with the science counselor and was discussing the logistics of my visit with his secretary when we heard a loud bang. Alarms went off and smoke began to fill the hallway. A Marine came running in and moved us to an interior room. We were convinced that a rifle grenade had been fired into the Embassy. Eventually, the all-clear was sounded. The commotion had been due to a short circuit in a fuse box in the ancient electrical system of the old palazzo.

The next few days were filled with a continuous series of meetings and inspections of laboratory facilities punctuated by hours of solitude in my room. When Saturday came along, I decided to go out into the town. I hoped to pick up some books and look for a pair of fine leather shoes and a silk tie at the shops in the Via Corso.

As I walked along, I followed routine procedures to ensure that I was not being followed. I casually scanned the faces of passersby, noting whether a particular face kept appearing at different locations. This was singularly unproductive since foreign travelers tend to gravitate towards certain urban locations. Quite innocently, the same people appear again and again. Glancing at shop windows, I checked the reflections for anyone showing unusual interest in my movements. I walked into a large store through one entrance and exited through another, checking that I was not being followed. Nothing suspicious. Reassured, I stood at a bar sipping a cappuccino and savoring the morning sun. The next stop was the English language bookstore in the Piazza di Spagna. Emerging with a shopping bag full of paperbacks, I took my time going up the Spanish Steps to the church of Trinita dei Monti, where I dallied for part of an hour.

I was coming down the steps when three young well-dressed children came running up, screaming at the top of their voices, and waving pieces of cardboard in my face. I froze for several seconds before noticing a small hand reaching into the inside pocket of my jacket which contained nothing more valuable than a street map. My reflexes kicked in. I moved to place my back against the wall, bellowed loudly as I swung my bag of books in a semicircle in front of me. The children jumped back and were gone as rapidly as they had appeared. No terrorists, just wayward children at their pickpocket trade.

Rather shaken, I changed my plans and returned to the hotel, stopping on the way to buy a panini and a juice drink. While picking up my room key, I saw that the clerk was glued to the television set. The image of President Reagan appeared for a few seconds before shifting to films of fighter jets taking off and bombs hitting an unknown target. The clerk turned to me.

"Signor, serious news. President Reagan has just been speaking."

"Why? What happened?"

"American planes have just bombed Libya in retaliation for the terrorist acts by Gaddafi. The Libyans have accused Italy of providing assistance to the Americans and they threaten to retaliate. Let us hope that nothing happens in Rome."

Not at all reassured, I hunkered down in my room for the rest of the day. At least I had plenty to read.

By 8 p.m. I was starving, frazzled with worry about the imagined threats to my safety, and wondering what to do for dinner since the hotel had no restaurant. My strategy was to stay in the Via Veneto area where there were plenty of people and police, and since I was Chinese I would not be identified as an American diplomat. To take it a step further, I chose a Japanese restaurant. Any Palestinian hitman would take me for an Osaka businessman in need of a sushi fix. Calmed down, I went out and walked down the Via Veneto feeling comfortable amongst all the pedestrians. I turned onto the side street that led to my restaurant. As I did so, I noticed that two young men, well dressed in suits, seemed to be following me. As taught, I changed my pace. When I slowed down, they did so also. As I quickened my pace, they did the same. Then they accelerated and split up, one moving to my left, the other to my right.

The young man on my right moved close, putting his left arm over my shoulder and said, "Buona sera, signor. Your first time in Rome?"

My heart froze. I recalled a scenario from one of the briefings. A way to assassinate someone in a busy street is to put an arm around the shoulder of the target, and stab him on the opposite side with a long thin blade right under the armpit. The accomplice on the other side keeps the victim moving forward until coming to a place where he can prop the body in a doorway or an alley. Panicked, I looked around the street for other people. There were some, but no one close by. Then, out of the corner of my eye, I saw a movement towards my jacket. Oh, God, here it comes. But wait, he's really trying to reach the inner pocket of my jacket. I pivoted, pushed the other fellow away, and moved to place my back against the wall of a building, swung wildly, and yelled for help, "Aiuto! Aiuto!"

Heads turned, the two guys took off and disappeared, leaving me to catch my breath and slow down my racing heart. Just another robbery attempt.

My mission in Italy completed with my life intact, I toured Toulouse, one of France's high technology cities, then returned to London. As required, I met with the Regional Security Officer to be debriefed. The RSO looked up from a file on his desk.

"Hello, Professor. I see that your trip went well. But you must be glad to be back. Did you have any incidents or suspicious events to report? Particularly in Italy?"

"The trip was very successful. No security problems. But you fellows should be congratulated. While I cannot vouch for the efficacy of the methods to foil assassination attempts, they work marvelously well against pickpockets and thieves."

It was common for me to be on the road for weeks at a time. Each day was filled with meetings, interviews, site visits, business meals. When I got back to my hotel at the end of the day, I would work on my notes and cable and country reports. The challenge was to find quiet private moments to explore my surroundings and pursue my own interests.

Once, after I had spent several days at a conference in Florence, I paid a call to the US consul to thank him for the logistical support he had provided to me. I was tired and rather tense. He asked whether I had any plans before going on to Rome. I laughed and said that my plans were to make calls to Washington and catch up on my sleep. When he suggested that I spend the weekend in Venice before proceeding on to Rome, I was cool to the idea. I had been to Venice several times and had found it expensive, vastly overrated, and overrun with unruly tourists and dishonest locals. Nevertheless, he convinced me that it was different in winter, when you could experience the real Venice in all its glory. He had taken the liberty to book me into one of his favorite hotels, a few steps from the Piazza San Marco.

So there I was in the Hotel Flora on a Saturday afternoon, reading a mystery and thinking on what to do with my evening. I decided on dinner at the venerable Hotel Danieli, which required a reservation and a jacket and tie. I was in the mood for a simple meal, an appetizer of gnocchi with ragu sauce, an entrée of veal filet with an accompaniment of carrots and watercress, and a bottle of classical Valpolicella from the Lago di Garda, reminiscent of a Beaujolais nouveau. After dinner I walked out into a cool, misty night and strolled over to Harry's Bar by the Piazza San Marco, where I sat in my trench coat and slowly savored an expresso and a cognac.

The Piazza was enveloped in fog and shadow with only a few old waiters and lonely tourists. It was the very image of wintry solitude. Suddenly, a burst of shouting broke the silence as a hundred university students came rushing into the Piazza. They made a large circle in the square placing their bags and knapsacks in the middle. The clapping of hands and the tapping of feet set a compelling rhythm that seemed surreal in the night and fog. I could tell from their shouts and singing that the young dancers were from Spain. As the music accelerated, I and the other few spectators joined in with our clapping. There was something very familiar about the dance – it brought back memories of summers spent in Calella, a small village in the Costa Brava of Spain. It was the sardana, a Catalan folk dance, an elegant almost courtly dance that brought together young and old, men and women, in the town square. And here it was, in a moment worthy of a Fellini or a Spielberg: the Piazza San Marco, the dark, misty night that kept the tourists away, the old waiters from Harry's Bar, the lithe young Catalan dancers moving to the rhythm of the sardana. What could be more perfect? When it came to an end, waiters, visitors, locals, students, all applauded with spirit.

On another occasion, after a meeting with the CEO of an Italian multinational, he asked me whether I had any plans for lunch. If I had the time, he would like to take me for lunch at a restaurant in the countryside outside of Milan. We were met by the owner, who asked whether we would trust him to organize the luncheon. Of course we did. It consisted of a spinach salad with a caviar dressing, a grilled sea bass, along with a bottle of champagne. And for dessert, perfectly ripe pears and cheese. It was all beautifully simple in a quiet rural setting accompanied by urbane conversation. We enjoyed a special moment in a foreign land basking in the generosity and kindness of a stranger. All these years later, I can recall vividly this moment of simple perfection.

The Human Touch

Then there are those moments that represent a test of one's identity. I was called to the office of DAS Kelley before I flew to my London posting.

We had a polite exchange in which he wished me success on my new project. Then he got to the real point of the meeting. "You should no longer think of yourself as being White, Asian, Hispanic, Black. You are now a diplomat and represent the United States of America. Do not ever forget that."

There were two instances in which his advice was put to the test. I had reported to the Commercial Counselor at one of the major US embassies. I had a temporary duty assignment with visits to several cities, and all the necessary orders had been sent from Washington and the London Embassy. I was therefore shocked and surprised when the Counselor launched into a long tirade about my assignment and questioned my qualifications. Worst of all, he emphasized that he could not waste his valuable resources to carry out my project. I believe that he had been taken by surprise by my Asian identity and that he had reacted with his gut. His refusal to collaborate would thwart my assignment. Two weeks of meetings and inspections would have to be canceled and, with them, this country report. I was deeply upset and at a loss, uncertain about how to proceed. I chose to go by the book: I emphasized the orders from Washington and the London Embassy as well as the supporting documents for my project and my professional qualifications. Instinctively, I knew I had to make it clear that there would be a cost for his behavior. I quietly said that I would notify DAS Kelley that I could not proceed with the project. He should also cable Kelley that he could not follow the order to provide support for my assignment. I knew that he could not refuse an order from Washington in the absence of due cause.

The Counselor remained silent for moments, then called his personal assistant and told her to work with me for the coming weeks. My work continued as normal, as if that moment had never occurred, and I was not to see him again until I signed out from his Embassy.

For the most part, I would be traveling in the Continent during the week, usually flying back to Heathrow on one of the last Friday night flights. I would collect my luggage and go through one of the special Immigration lanes for diplomatic personnel. Most of the time, I would be waved right through. Rarely, an agent might glance at my diplomatic passport. One night, the inspector examined my passport and asked,

"Are you in transit?"

A rather pointless question since I was not in the transit section. I replied that I was posted to the US Embassy in London. He requested additional documents. I gave him my Embassy ID card and a Foreign Office pass that showed I was accredited to Her Majesty's government. He started questioning me.

"Are you located at the Embassy or the consular offices?"

"Are you in the diplomatic service or administrative?"

"What are your job responsibilities?"

I was tired and tense after a long week and knew fully well that the Geneva Agreement allowed me free passage and that his behavior was very much in the nature of personal harassment. So I looked at him and said quietly,

"You are in violation of the Geneva Agreement as regards diplomatic personnel. So I suggest we do the following: Get the immigration officer in charge, allow me to phone the duty officer at the US Embassy to report this situation."

He glared at me, handed back my documents, and waved me on in a huff. I was again dramatically reminded of what DAS Kelley had told me, and acted in a way compliant with my status as a US Foreign Service officer.

In preparing for my project, I had been often told that France would be one of the more difficult countries to work in. The French were seen as prickly and not very open to sharing information. My experience was clearly different.

One of my priorities was to meet Jean Jacques Salomon, an expert on the interaction between science, technology and society. He had been the French delegate to the OECD and was involved in the French plan for biotechnology. He had also authored a major work on French biotechnology in comparison with the US and Japan. The Embassy had not been able to arrange an interview with him. Jean Comar was one of the principal drivers of biotechnology in France through his support for start-up biotech companies and publication of biotech stories, particularly in his journal *Bio-Futur*. I had been introduced to him by an American friend who was CEO of a biotech company and had collaborated with Comar. I went to Paris on a Sunday and spent the day with him and his partner discussing the wide world of biotechnology. He took me for a quiet and elegant dinner on the Left Bank. We ended up discussing Salomon, and he promised to arrange a meeting.

Days later, I met Salomon in his office. It was one of those occasions when I debated in my mind whether to carry out the conversation in French or English. I chose French, and for more than two hours, we shared much of our knowledge. I particularly appreciated his critical views of the situation in France. At the end, I asked him how I could gain access to his new report. He smiled, walked over to a cupboard that had multiple copies of his report, took one out and dedicated it to me.

When I returned to the Embassy, the science counselor asked me how the meeting had gone. I gave him a very positive response and showed him my copy of Salomon's report. He immediately had it copied and sent to Washington.

Biotechnology in Western Europe

My biotechnology assessment of Western Europe took place over a period of 17 months and covered France, Germany, Italy, Netherlands, Norway, Finland, Denmark, Sweden, Spain, Switzerland, and the United Kingdom.

The general view was that biotechnology and information technology would transform economies worldwide. In the major countries such as the U.K., France, and Germany, the research required more than one visit, while in some of the smaller countries, the efforts focused on selected research laboratories and private firms. The basic findings were that in selected areas of basic research, work in European laboratories was world class. In Western Europe, the impact of biotechnology in industry was driven by government policies and investment. This was in sharp contrast to the US where basic research findings in universities and institutes were used to start up new companies funded by venture capital. In the US, the commercialization of a new technology generated a variety of business models, some of which would be highly profitable.

Some of the most important European countries had established national biotechnology programs where the government was directly involved at all levels, from basic research to commercialization. Of particular significance were the programs in applied R&D, such as technology transfer institutes, and funding in universities, research institutes, and private companies. In aspects of industrial policy, government provided tax credits for industrial R&D, loans and grants for new processes and products, and risk capital for new companies.

More Decisions

The original plan was for me to return to the University of Maryland by the fall of 1986. By midsummer, it was time for me to schedule my last round of meetings and visits mainly to Scandinavia, wrapping up my affairs in London in September and then heading home. However, both Washington and the new commercial counselor wanted me to extend my stay by a few more months. And then another rather tempting alternative emerged. The position of science counselor had opened up in Beijing, and Bob Stella, the science counselor in London, thought I should apply for it. On the other hand, Sam Joseph, my department chair back at College Park, wanted me to return in October. This put me under considerable stress since I was uncertain about my return to an academic career, and my marriage to Ying-Ying was coming to an end. Returning to the US was less about going home than it was about trying to find a new life. I decided to come back to the United States.

The end of my diplomatic assignment came in a flurry of reporting cables, partial drafts on my report on biotechnology in Western Europe, briefings, and yes, even farewell parties. In the quiet interludes, I took time to reflect on what I had accomplished, learned, and felt over the past seventeen months overseas. Assessing the outcomes from an official perspective was not difficult: there were comprehensive reports on eleven countries in Western Europe, along with the European initiatives. It covered R&D, government policy, industry, finance, and technology transfer. There was no other equivalent report at that time.

At a personal level, I had been able to design an approach for the study of how different countries made use of biotechnology to promote their economic development. Since neither State nor Commerce had much experience in such studies, I had first to train myself and then to implement the project without much advice from others. I was not concerned about my understanding of basic science since I had been doing research all my life and was familiar with what was happening both in the US and abroad. Learning about the emerging US biotech industry (particularly in the small new firms) and the workings of venture capital funds had been a different matter. In the first months of the project, we visited a significant number of companies and financial groups to familiarize ourselves with US biotechnology.

The single biggest challenge had been to develop a strategy for working with the Foreign Service professionals at the embassies and the contacts in the foreign countries. A natural introvert, I was uncomfortable interacting with senior individuals whom I was meeting for the first time. With the American diplomats, I found it best to keep a low profile and to make them feel that as we made progress, it would not only benefit my bosses in Washington but also the embassies that were supporting our work. I made sure that I shared my information with the diplomats so that it could be incorporated into the embassy reporting cables and, in many cases, had them join me in important meetings with senior business executives and government officials.

I would like to believe that my activities relating to a revolutionary new technology such as biotechnology provided an element of excitement to the normal world of diplomacy. I could never have survived nor done as much as I did without the friendship and support of Al Hellman in Washington, Bob Stella, the science counselor, and Michael Mercurio, the commercial attaché in London.

Two different aspects were less successful. One objective was to use the information from the competitive study to promote the US biotechnology companies particularly in developing external markets. This would have been the responsibility of the domestic offices of the Foreign Commercial Service, but high technology industry was not one of FCS's strengths, and their efforts were sporadic at best. Another objective from the perspective of Washington was to increase the role of US embassies in increasingly important areas such as science and technology, high tech industrial development, and regulatory frameworks.

This was problematic in two important respects: senior embassy officials were not particularly comfortable with those of us who were not career Foreign Service officers and who delved into exotic technical matters that were beyond the officials' comprehension. Furthermore, the technology and industrial functions were not integrated into the structure of the State Department, so that at best our projects were short term.

One thing I learned is that whatever doubts people may have about the power and influence of the US, people in authority take the US seriously. Wherever I was, the US Embassy was able to arrange a meeting with the most important academics, government officials, and corporate executives.

In principle, obtaining information and insights from foreign VIP's was similar to the work with Americans. There were two very important differences (that were even more critical in my later work in Asia): language and cultural exposure. In my debriefing, I was asked repeatedly whether knowledge of foreign languages was important in carrying out my mission. My reply was that almost all foreign leaders that dealt with science and technology and high tech industries were fluent in English. Having said that, I was happy to have the choice to use English or the local language. For example, if I chose to use French or Spanish (languages in which I am comfortably fluent), the energy of the conversation would change. This is partly because nuance is tricky in a foreign language. That fear of being misunderstood can be inhibiting, but is alleviated when you are using your own language. My ability to communicate effectively in a variety of languages greatly enhanced the efficacy of the work we were doing.

The other important element is that using the local language opens the door to social interactions that go beyond science or policy. I do not know how many times my interlocutor would suggest that we go to a neighboring bistro for a drink or perhaps if I was free for dinner, we could go to a local restaurant owned by a friend. This enabled me to have an open conversation where projects or initiatives could be framed as challenges or problems and we could discuss what worked or did not work. Those assessments were independent of nationality and country. And a small personal gift (a bottle of fine malt whiskey, an Ansel Adams print, a book on Chinese culture) or a copy of a paper or a book would be deeply appreciated as a gesture of friendship and collegiality.

Lessons Learned

During this relatively brief period, I underwent a major transformation in my career and skills. More importantly, I lived a different way of life which changed the way I saw the world around me.

Joining the Foreign Service required the acquisition of a large body of information about the countries where I would be working. Perhaps just as important was to become familiar with the rules and procedures of the State Department. Designing an international technology assessment project that could be implemented within the context of State Department procedures and with the active support and cooperation of individual US embassies required a merging of two very different cultures: science and technology with government policy. It also required a change in my personality from quiet and reticent observer to outgoing, socially engaging, and more articulate extrovert. This was an enormous challenge.

As a diplomat, I learned the importance of the personal touch. I acquired a deep respect for the professionalism and dedication of American Foreign Service officers whose help and support were essential for my work. I made sure that the names of my collaborators in the embassies would appear in my cables and reports. I always found time to write personal notes to all my foreign interlocutors who had generously given me their time and information. And copies of the final reports were sent to them.

Their reactions could be quite personal and amusing. In the case of the French report (which had been relatively critical), one of the French officials phoned me and remarked that given the tone of the report, I might never get a French visa again. Then he emphasized that he was joking. But then I found out that he had ordered twenty copies of the report. When I asked him, he remarked that no equivalent French report would be so objective and candid!

What is more, I honed some skills that turned out to be invaluable in the years ahead: time management and multitasking in an interdisciplinary and global context. My travel schedule and task assignments meant that I had to make use of every time window. A room service dinner allowed me to work on my notes, working on those notes could be combined with drafting a cable. The length of a flight determined whether there was time to translate a document. The ability to steal a catnap between meetings was a saving grace. Most important of all was to achieve a balance between work and leisure when on the road. It required seeking out and finding those activities that I truly enjoyed, that helped keep me sane and rested. This balance became an essential part of my time-management system: an early morning walk, time for a quiet read, a night at the opera, a winter weekend in Venice. Under those circumstances, these isolated moments were no longer a luxury but became a necessity.

The cathedral and Rhine Bridge
Basel, Switzerland

Biozentrum Basel

Werner Arber and Bob

Al and Kiki Hellman
with Bob at a press conference
Vienna, 1986

University
of Maryland,
College Park

Tsukuba Science Center
Japan

New Bridge
Ronda, Spain

Great Mosque
Cordoba, Spain

The old man
and the sea

Lunch
Bagnoregio,
Italy

Michael Ma, Nikki,
and Yuan
San Juan

Nikki and Bob
Australia

Bob and his father
2002

Desert at dawn

GOING GLOBAL
Washington D.C. and Asia
1986 - 1988

By the end of 1986, it was time to make another decision. Fujimura and I had completed our studies of biotechnology in Western Europe and Japan. I had left my position at the US Embassy in London and returned to Washington. I could take up my professorship at the University of Maryland at College Park, I could pursue further studies for the Department of Commerce, or I could figure out how to do both.

This was not easy. I had changed, the world was changing at warp speed, but the university remained mired in its old ways. The chair of my department and my faculty colleagues could not conceive of research except in its traditional laboratory form, and I was required to do a certain amount of regular teaching.

There were discussions at the Department of Commerce regarding a new series of studies in Asia that would include China and the newly industrializing countries of Taiwan, South Korea, Singapore, and Hong Kong plus additional work on Japan. These foreign projects fell into a few categories: a continuation of the studies for the US government, contracts for foreign governments and private companies, the organization of international conferences, and the writing of a biotechnology column. Unfortunately, these types of projects did not fit into my traditional duties of research and teaching. However, because the provost and the president were supportive of these new initiatives, I proposed to create a consulting group that allowed us to do international projects while giving the university public exposure and overhead payments. In the process, I was changing my job description at the university.

The Asian Miracle

Our first project involved a new series of biotechnology studies in Asia. My preliminary analysis focused on the landmark World Bank study, "The Asian Economic Miracle," which examined the principal factors that led to the emergence of the modern Asian economies. This included a diverse group of countries including Japan as the new economic superpower, a group of newly industrializing countries like South Korea, Singapore, and Taiwan, and the emerging giant of China. Government policy had been a major driver as was the choice of selected industries for competition in the world market. Expert opinion believed that Japan was the economic model for its Asian neighbors.

The Asian project was operationally and conceptually very different from my earlier European one. Since I was no longer a foreign service officer on a government project, I could not make use of the US embassies and their resources. Logistically, I needed to operate from my base in Washington, making long trips to Asia. I had my own team and often got logistical support from foreign governments, coordinating my research with the US missions. The research I had done in Europe had introduced me to a whole new world that combined government policy, technology, industry, and economic development. In the process, I had acquired a new knowledge base and set of skills totally different from my previous scientific career. Europe was a familiar terrain, where I was well acquainted with its scientific establishment and had a network of useful contacts.

I had serious concerns as to the Asian project both conceptually and logistically. While these Asian countries had been successful in manufacturing and gaining access to Western markets, it remained uncertain whether they would succeed in such high technology fields as biotechnology. Each of these countries also had a distinctive history and culture. The scientific establishments, economic structures, and government policies were not only very different from those of the US but were also changing at incredible speed. Not only did I have to learn about all these countries, but I had to establish new sets of contacts. Perhaps more than anywhere else in the world, connections were all important. Up to this point, I had been most comfortable in an American/West European cultural environment. But this changed as I tried to understand the way in which Asia was moving into modernity while retaining ancient cultural traditions and evolving its own democratic institutions.

I worked long and hard to establish the necessary procedures for my Asian project. I assembled a team that consisted of Yuan Lin, Michael Ma, Michael Hsu, Po Chi Wu. All of them were fluent in Chinese and expert in biotechnology. Yuan Lin, was from Taiwan, had a background in genetic engineering, and we had taught a faculty workshop in Taiwan. Michael Ma was a colleague from the University of Maryland specializing in agricultural biotechnology. Po Chi Wu was a venture capitalist with a background in biotechnology and work experience in China, Hong Kong, and Taiwan. The most fascinating character was Michael Hsu, who ran Asia Pacific Bioventures in New York, spent time in Taipei, Bangkok, and Kuala Lumpur, and raised capital throughout Asia. He was a large man, often known as the Big Chinaman. He was a veritable fountain of knowledge, full of energy and great fun to work with. Since his business interests were far and wide, he gave us access to his extensive network of contacts. I devised a strategy of getting to know senior officials at selected embassies in Washington who usually belonged to the Ministry of Science and Technology or the Ministry of Industry. Through them I got to work with their counterparts in their home countries.

The Little Tigers: Singapore, South Korea and Taiwan

At the end of the 1980s, I launched a study involving three emerging Asian economies entitled "Biotechnology in Singapore, South Korea and Taiwan." A study of Hong Kong was to be carried out later as part of a separate project on China. South Korea and Taiwan were under authoritarian regimes while Singapore had a form of controlled democracy. The basic research establishments in the three countries were a work in progress. A major priority was the creation of new research centers by the government, while the universities focused on education. The major limiting factor in the development of both R&D and the biotechnology industry was a shortage of professional manpower. Taiwan was in the strongest position, while Singapore had the most visible shortage of biological scientists. The most rapid solution to this problem was the active recruitment of expatriate scientists, mostly from the US. Singapore had used a policy of high salaries and excellent laboratory facilities to try to create a world class scientific establishment. Even so, if the shortage of scientists throughout Asia was already serious, the problem was even more pronounced when it came to senior managers.

In general, the manufacturing industries in these countries had a remarkable record of success. Agriculture, aquaculture, food processing, and the fermentation industries were commercially important, while the biotechnology industry was in its infancy. Singapore and Taiwan were both committed to the creation of new biotechnology companies, whereas South Korea directed its new industrial activities to its large conglomerates.

Though the governments encouraged the activities of multinational companies, they realized that they were not likely to introduce new technologies or products. One of the primary objectives of these governments was to promote new companies following different models: a) companies closely associated with government institutions (Taiwan), b) companies that were part of industrial conglomerates (South Korea), and c) new companies that were frequently joint ventures with US companies (Japan). Each country had an active entrepreneurial environment, particularly in Singapore and Taiwan. Investment capital was plentiful but there was little experience with R&D-dependent companies. Financial institutions associated with the government therefore played a major role in the funding of biotechnology business. The single most important challenge in the industrial development of biotechnology was the creation of an integrated team of scientists, managers, and marketing specialists. Singapore fared best in this respect, as it had an international environment as well as a competitive salary structure.

The Rise of China

The Department of Commerce project represented a special opportunity to carry out research in China, and its timing could not have been more exciting. My next study was "Biotechnology in the People's Republic of China and Hong Kong," which I carried out with Yuan Lin. By 1988, China had begun its major reforms in a transition to a more capitalist economy. It addressed two major issues: the evolution of China's political and economic structure and its use of technology to modernize itself. One important reform was the change from a political leadership to a scientific one. The government of the PRC had selected biotechnology as one of its key high technology sectors. China's science and technology establishment followed the model of the Soviet Union where research was mainly conducted in the institutes of the various academies, in particular the Chinese Academy of Sciences. Very little research was carried out at the universities.

The research infrastructure was weak due to outdated facilities and management practices. The China National Center for Biotechnology Development was created to fund specific areas of applied research in biotechnology and to coordinate the activities of the diverse institutes and laboratories. The priorities were in biomedicine, agriculture, and protein engineering. The emphasis was on projects that were likely to affect large numbers of people, e.g., development of new diagnostics, vaccines, and insect- and disease-resistance in crop plants. Most of the biomedical research was derivative and followed general directions set in the US, Europe, and Japan. In agriculture, the Chinese had drawn on their experience in plant tissue culture and plant breeding to develop much more innovative projects in gene transfer.

The Chinese understood the need to reform the universities by introducing research laboratories, new PhD programs, and even small companies. International cooperation was all important particularly as related to training and financing. The best graduates from Chinese universities were sent abroad (mainly to the US) for advanced studies and research and then returned to provide important scientific leadership. Chinese laboratories had limited budgets, and grants and contracts from foreign sources were an important source of foreign exchange used in the purchase of reagents and equipment unavailable in China.

China's pharmaceutical industry was all important in meeting the nation's health needs. It operated at full capacity with favorable profit margins, but was far from modern. At the time, a novel initiative was the joint venture between Squibb, based in New York City, and China's State Pharmaceutical Organization. Shanghai Squibb manufactured antibiotics, vitamins, and cardiovascular drugs. While sales had been good, there were serious problems with the need to import raw materials and the lack of patent protection. Chinese companies had pirated some of Squibb's products and sold them in the Chinese market.

China represented an interesting possibility for the application of biotechnology. As the Chinese economy grew, it provided a huge market for pharmaceutical and agricultural/food products as well as a platform for exports. The export market could only be realized if the Chinese products met international regulatory standards and patents. And the emergence of this modern industry required a skilled labor force, technology, and capital investment. Joint ventures were key reforms that would transform the Chinese economy.

Japan

The series of biotechnology studies in Asia was completed with a study on Japan done by myself and Mark Dibner of the North Carolina Biotechnology Center. This was a follow-up on the earlier DOC report. Dibner had extensive experience on Japanese biotechnology and had put together a comprehensive data base on the Japanese biotechnology industry. The project was funded by a group of four states and the IC2/RGK Foundation and KPMG Peat Marwick. At this point, Japan was the world's second major economic power, and it had selected biotechnology as a key industrial technology for the future. Japan's greatest strength in biotechnology was in industry. Many of Japan's largest firms were using biotechnology to innovate in their traditional businesses (e.g., enzymes in detergents) or to expand into new fields (e.g., pharmaceuticals, waste treatment). Though the market for new biotechnology products had grown slowly, Japanese companies had the resources to develop and commercialize biotechnology. In many instances, new products and technologies were developed through strategic alliances with US companies.

The Japanese government had developed policies to promote biotechnology. The basic research in the biological sciences was pursued mainly in the universities and the national laboratories. The industry had established new private research institutes by itself or in collaboration with government institutes with increasing government and industrial funding. Nevertheless, basic research in key areas such as molecular immunology and plant biotechnology lagged behind the US and key countries in Western Europe. This weakness in R&D was due primarily to the structure of both public and private research institutes which provided few opportunities for young researchers to initiate their own projects and work in an interdisciplinary mode.

The competitive relationship between the US and Japan was ambiguous. Japanese firms had a strong need for US technology and novel products, while new US biotechnology companies were in search of capital to support their R&D programs. Both sides sought strategic alliances but in terms that gave each of them a significant advantage.

At the end of the 20th century neither China nor the newly industrialized countries were considered to be important players in the world of high technology. Today, Japan and China, South Korea, Hong Kong, Taiwan, Singapore and the overseas communities in Southeast Asia play an ever more important economic global role.

Expanding the Scope: Hong Kong and Thailand

The biotechnology reports for the US government had attracted the attention of other governments that then approached me to commission similar projects. These studies typically had two components. One was an evaluation of the national resources available for promoting biotechnology in the country (e.g., research activities, government policy). The other involved plans and recommendations for the use of biotechnology to promote economic development, usually in the biomedical and agricultural sectors. These territories (Hong Kong and Thailand) were very different in their political frameworks, economies, and plans for a technological future. Hong Kong played a traditional role as the interface between China and the West and was in the process of returning to Chinese rule. Its importance had been as a financial and trading center. Thailand was becoming a newly industrializing country with a successful agricultural economy. Politically, they were very distinct from each other.

I was not familiar with either of them, so my research would require a great deal of groundwork and changes in methodology. I did have some advantages in that I had done an earlier study on Hong Kong, and I was familiar with the basic characteristics of Chinese culture. When working in Thailand, I realized that the Chinese community played an important role in business and technology. And though it would take time to identify those of Chinese origin, they would be forthcoming and helpful when they found out that I was Chinese-American.

Hong Kong

The project in Hong Kong was of particular importance in that Hong Kong was developing a new role in relation to mainland China. This British Crown Colony was in the process of returning to Chinese rule in 1997. Our study examined how Hong Kong was likely to function as an autonomous zone once it came under Chinese rule.

The economic success of Hong Kong had been based on its light manufacturing, its role as an intermediary between the PRC and the outside world, and as an Asian financial center. Hong Kong's small size limited the resources available for the build-up of biotechnology. Its biotechnology activities were centered in two of its universities, the Chinese University of Hong Kong and the University of Hong Kong, to which the Hong Kong University of Science and Technology had just been added. HKUST's main efforts were educational. A major initiative was the creation of the Hong Kong Biotechnology Institute. Its principal mission was to select projects with high industrial potential, do the applied research, and then transfer the results to private industry in Hong Kong or China. Its research staff would partly come from the PRC. A second biotechnology institute was planned for the Hong Kong University of Science and Technology.

There was no biotechnology industry, but there were plenty of firms that manufactured food products. Traditional Chinese Medicine was a significant business, but it mainly involved the trade of medicinal herbs and formulations and their export to Asia. The far bigger opportunity was to use the Chinese formulations as the basis for new Western drugs. The project required us to make visits to China, Taiwan, Singapore, and Thailand which were likely to be important sources for scientific and commercial collaboration.

Working for the Hong Kong government was fundamentally different from our earlier projects for the US government. In addition to my team, I had an excellent Hong Kong team from the Department of Industry with a deep knowledge of the territory. Our work was supervised by the Committee on Science and Technology made up of scientists and academics headed by Professor K. C. Li. Our recommendations were based on a model where Hong Kong would be a major financial center and a center for the transfer of biotechnology applications to China and other Asian countries. This would require expanding research at the universities, increasing technology transfer at three of its centers, and funding of biotechnology in private industry. Such efforts proposed an increase in government budgets and a reorganization of government functions.

The role of Hong Kong would change following its return to China in 1997. Though it was still an underdeveloped country, China had huge potential. Hong Kong could play a central role as the interface with the West providing access to technology, skilled manpower, and capital. How this could be implemented remained a mystery.

Thailand

Thailand was my first experience working in a developing country. It had been a major recipient of US economic assistance. One of its programs had funded research at Thai universities with the objective of transferring new technology to industry and agriculture. This approach had not been successful.

I proposed a new program which identified commercial opportunities for biotechnology in Thailand. Our objective was to find US firms with the appropriate products/processes and match them with potential Thai partners. On the US side we worked with the US National Research Council and on the Thai side with the National Science and Technology Development Agency. This UST/COST program brought together 15 US companies with Thai partners involving food and agriculture development. This approach to technology transfer was innovative, since it was based on existing technologies and direct agreements between US and Thai firms. It had also provided us with an opportunity to work on technology transfer in a developing country.

A Chinese World

My first site visit on the Asian project had been to Singapore, a totally novel experience. This modern city state had successfully incorporated the government, business, and educational practices of advanced Western countries. Even though majority Chinese, it was a multicultural society that brought together Chinese, Malaysians, Indians, and Westerners. Over time, I realized that there were many aspects of Singapore that reminded me of Switzerland, which was also multicultural and international, and whose guiding principles were that it worked and was on time. I began to realize that it was possible to live simultaneously in two distinct modes: Chinese and Western.

Taiwan was quite different in that it was distinctly Chinese but perhaps more akin to pre-Communist society. I developed many working relationships and friendships and served in various review and advisory committees. Since many of my Taiwanese colleagues had studied and worked in the US, it did not feel all that different from the US except in a Chinese social environment. Food was an essential part of the culture, so a great deal of our discussions and transactions were carried out over meals.

Hong Kong was again different. It shared with Singapore the heritage of British rule and its identity as a city, but here the Chinese identity was more regional. Many of the residents had come from Guangzhou and Shanghai with a keen sense of business and trade. Much of Hong Kong reminded me of New York: high energy, creative, iconoclastic, and also endowed with a wicked sense of humor. In those years, I felt more and more Chinese but was also conscious that these were individual Chinese cultures that were distinct from that in mainland China. Here language again played a role. Most younger Chinese spoke Mandarin but in given groups they would use dialect (e.g., Cantonese or, in Taiwan, the Taiwanese dialect). In time, the question would come up (sometimes in jest, sometimes seriously) of whether I would be willing to relocate to Asia. It was a complicated notion since it not only involved a different working environment, but also a drastic change in my personal life. My Chinese friends seemed to take that in stride. I remember the director of an institute just smiling and saying, "We can always introduce you to a new girlfriend and you can start a new life here."

The Public Face of Biotechnology in Asia

Our work increased the interest of governments and firms in biotechnology in Asia. This resulted in two long-term initiatives. One was a biennial conference on "Biotechnology in the Pacific Rim." Such conferences brought together research scientists, government officials, industry executives, and financiers. The objective was to promote research in biotechnology and its use in agriculture and industry.

Early in my research, I had noticed the efficient way in which Asian technocrats worked, in sharp contrast with our much more bureaucratic approach. I first brought up the idea of the biotechnology conferences at a meeting with the Singapore Economic Development Board. Foo Meng Tong, director of the Industry Development Division, approached me during the break. He told me how much he liked the idea, suggesting that the first conference be held in Singapore and that his government would be willing to fund it. And so it happened. Starting in 1988, such conferences were held in Singapore, Houston, Taiwan, Seoul, San Diego, and Hong Kong. Such venues were important in bringing together influential individuals committed to developing biotechnology in the Pacific Rim. I was involved in the organization of most of those meetings.

The American way of coming to an agreement is data driven, supported by documentation, financials, and legal papers. On the Asian side, it was far more important that the principals get to know and trust each other. They could then come to an agreement, and the details could be filled in by staff. Michael Hsu always told the story of taking the head of a Boston financial group to Taipei to meet with his Chinese counterpart. The American pushed hard to get to closure on the deal. The Chinese banker turned to Michael and said quietly, "Tell your friend that he will have to consume a lot of green tea before we have a deal."

Soon after I started work on the Singapore conference, I was approached by John Sterling, the managing editor of *Genetic Engineering News*, the major biotechnology journal. He invited me to write a regular column on "Biotechnology in the Pacific Rim." I approached Michael Hsu and we became co-authors. This column became an essential source of information on the increasing importance of biotechnology in the economies of these Asian nations. Writing a column taught me how to incorporate brevity and clarity into my articles. I acquired interviewing skills and gained a broader perspective. And, as my readership grew, so did the story leads that ended up on my desk.

The decision to remain at the university made it possible to pursue a portfolio of activities that now included studies on biotechnology in Asia, the organization of new and groundbreaking conferences, and a wide assortment of columns on biotechnology in Asia. To these would be added novel educational initiatives.

THE ART OF TEACHING
A Journey Without Maps
1986 - 2005

Long transpacific flights were an occupational hazard of my life in the 1990's as I worked on my Asian projects. Once comfortably installed in my seat, I would go through a predictable cycle of meals/snacks, sleep, reports, reading, and maybe a movie or two. Even after all that, I might still have another few hours before my plane landed in Washington. It was in those solitary hours that I began to reflect that the successful use of technology for economic development depended on the education of scientists and engineers. While I advised policy makers and faculty on the necessity for novel approaches to science and engineering education, I continued in my own classes to use traditional approaches of rote learning and testing that were singularly unproductive and resulted in high rates of student attrition.

Several factors deepened my interest in teaching. My father believed that teaching was the highest profession. He had taught briefly at Fudan University in Shanghai before joining the Chinese foreign service. Though he never realized his dream to become an academic, teaching was never far from his mind. For the Chinese, a master teacher possessed a deep knowledge of his field that was to be passed on to his students and used for the benefit of society. Two of my mentors, Meselson and Arber, exemplified my father's belief. They had not only been outstanding scientists themselves, but taught innovative undergraduate courses in genetics and molecular biology and were deeply committed to teaching. They were my models of scholar-teachers. Finally, I witnessed firsthand the deep need for major improvements in higher education. My projects in international biotechnology had shown me how ill prepared our students were for a rapidly changing world. Once again, it was time for me to dig in.

Science Education: The Reality of the Classroom

As a full professor, I started out by teaching some graduate courses, then moved into a couple of the large-enrollment undergraduate courses. The undergraduate courses were directed towards two very different groups of students. The science majors were supposed to learn the basic concepts and the laboratory skills to pursue the work. Non-science majors just needed an understanding of the basic concepts of biology to meet the requirements for an undergraduate degree. The attrition rates for science students are high, and non-science majors often do poorly and end up hating science.

My early teaching experiences at Maryland were not happy ones. My first course was General Microbiology, a large introductory undergraduate course. I found it an unrewarding experience consisting of lectures (organized around a textbook), cookbook lab experiments, and multiple-choice tests. The whole process rarely led to any real learning by the students. For example, the replication of DNA is an important concept that the students would retain long enough to pass their exams. It would have to be taught again in the mid-level courses, and then again at the senior level. Why? Because the students never mastered the concept, and most often would be unable to use it in any exercise in creative thinking. Unlike my work in research and technology policy, I found this type of teaching to be unproductive and devoid of intellectual challenge. Could it ever be otherwise?

After a couple of years, I rotated out of this course. But the way in which introductory courses were taught did not prepare the students for the more advanced courses. Perhaps even worse, students ended up hating science and dropping out. These were not problems that could be ignored since they were central to the organization of the science curriculum.

Microbes and Society was a large-enrollment biology course for non-science majors. This type of course has two negative consequences. Faculty perceive it as at the bottom of teaching choices; and the course is often assigned to part-time faculty. Many undergraduates are required to take it but typically learn very little. So it was against the odds that my friend, Spencer Benson, convinced me to take over this course. The question: Could I and my students learn anything from such a course?

I decided to experiment (I was a scientist, after all). I organized the course around a series of concepts linked to realities recognizable to students. For example, many living phenomena are due to microorganisms that cannot be readily seen or detected. The invention of the microscope and the growth of microorganisms on artificial media led to the detection and treatment of many infectious diseases (e.g., pneumonia) and the development of important industrial processes (e.g., pasteurization of milk, fermentation in the production of wine). The idea was to connect biological concepts to other topics. I also decided to replace final exams with a major essay in which the student was required to choose a major biological concept, explain it in his or her own words, and relate it to an important topic in his or her academic major.

The results were often thoughtful and imaginative. One student discussed her rather free-wheeling social life and analyzed the risks from sexually transmitted diseases and possible prevention strategies. A history major showed that in military campaigns, infectious diseases resulted in higher casualties than combat. A literature major wrote a short story on how intelligence genes could be inserted into a virus that could then be used to create more intelligent humans…with possible unintended consequences.

The course resulted in higher course averages, fewer dropouts, and favorable student evaluations. For me, this was a novel experience in that the students seemed to be more curious and able to connect biology to their own fields. This approach was far more challenging than droning my way through reams of dry information, but the results were so obviously positive that I considered my experiment a tremendous success.

Over the next two decades, education became an increasingly important part of my portfolio, divided into two distinct activities. One was defined by educational research, grants, and yes, academic politics. The other was more deeply personal, creating new courses and working closely with students to ensure their tangible growth and success.

A New Strategy for Science Education

Discussions with Bruce Alberts at the National Research Council involving projects related to biology education led me and Spencer Benson to write a concept paper on biology education. It was our view that the way in which science is done has changed radically. The reality is that our graduates go forth into a working environment characterized by interdisciplinary approaches to projects, teamwork and collaboration, multiple career options, the exponential growth of scientific information, and the global nature of science and technology. Traditional education was not setting students up to succeed in these areas.

The concept paper consisted of two parts, entitled "The Virtual Workplace" and "Journey Without Maps." It was our purpose in this paper to present a holistic curriculum for the 21st century. The "virtual workplace" provides students with a spectrum of thought processes and skills that prepares them for a variety of scientific and science-related careers. A "journey without maps" helps them to deal with the racial, ethnic, cultural, and economic diversity of the global environment.

The "Virtual Workplace" approach has been integrated into a set of undergraduate courses in which students ramp up their understanding of basic biological concepts and their acquisition of work skills. In content/process, students focus on a conceptual infrastructure that enables them to acquire and use information in the execution of their assigned tasks. They learn the skills of teamwork, data analysis, project design, writing, oral presentations, and peer review. We attempt to approximate the real-world work environment by the extensive use of electronic communications, increasing students' sensitivity to diversity, empowering the students to make certain decisions in the course, and making the course content relevant to their professional goals and personal objectives. This strategy has been incorporated into a set of courses that go from first-year to senior level courses.

"Journey Without Maps," which became the basis for three honors courses and, later, the East Asia Science and Technology (EAST) program, combines a set of interdisciplinary and cross-cultural courses, the development of cross-cultural teaching materials, and the use of mixed working teams. Our purpose was to go beyond the study of diversity and to provide, to the best of our ability, the experience of diversity.

Experimenting and the Diversity Notebook

Serving on a university committee, I got to know Sandy Mack, the director of the university's Honors Program. We discussed the ideas in our paper, and I proposed a new biology Honors seminar. The Diversity Notebook project had as its objective a course built around the concept of appropriate technology, i.e., the use of a process or product that is consistent with the culture and level of development of a particular society. Case studies were an essential pedagogical tool. We designed an Honors seminar, "Case Studies in Biology and Culture," using student teams which developed their own case studies (e.g., fermentation in soy sauce production, symbiosis in food poisoning from fish). The student team had to define the scientific problem (e.g., finding a diagnostic test to identify fish that cause food poisoning), evaluate possible solutions, and explore the economic, social, and cultural implications of such solutions. Case studies fell into three categories: medical, agricultural, and environmental. The experimental course included five pre-med students, and there was an extensive evaluation at its end. The use of interdisciplinary and cross-cultural case studies stimulated the learning of the science content because students had to research their own cases and find the relevance of the science to the society. Student comments showed the impact of the course:

- "With my other courses, I am reading a textbook. With this course I am … researching and writing my own textbook. These are our cases, and it is our responsibility to bring them to completion."

- "A critical aspect of dealing with AIDS in developing countries is having diagnostic tests. We use the ELISA test in the US, but learned of its limitations in places like Africa. In our discussions of ELISA, for the first time we understood the science and how it is used."

- "Their (science majors') tunnel vision … comes from other courses … and professors. This course reflects the world's reality. Diversity needs to be included in most other courses… the Diversity Notebook can benefit other students … I realized science had a real impact on real people … It changed the way I look at science."

- "At first it was not easy to approach Bob to test our findings and ideas. Then later, we were shy about writing or interviewing experts to get current information. But I was surprised that people were willing to help. We got good at it."
- "This is what real scientists do and it is hard. And sometimes there are no good solutions or they may be imperfect ones."

The nature of the case studies made the students look at the problems from different perspectives. For biology students, the common example for fermentation is the making of yogurt, and yet globally, the production of soy sauce is far more important economically and is an important step in the creation of a food industry in Asian countries. More dramatically, one of the teams dealt with the monitoring of biological weapons for arms control. Their conclusion was that technology allowed for detection of nuclear weapons from space, but to detect biological weapons required sampling on the ground. A few weeks later, a UN commission came to the same conclusions and recommended ground inspections in Iraq. It is hard to describe the excitement of the students. The problem was real, it was difficult, and the solution–as they had also concluded–was a compromise.

With the support of the University Honors Program, we converted the course into a regular Honors seminar with an enrollment of twenty students. I added one new aspect to the seminar in that I selected the four-person teams so that they were mixed by race, ethnicity, gender, and field of study. This brought different perspectives to each case study. The students could learn about diversity and globalization in scientific projects, and in the process create a collection of case studies that could be used in the introductory biology courses.

Broader Applications

The Honors Program was the perfect experimental platform in that its seminar courses were interdisciplinary and provided us with intelligent and motivated students from a variety of majors and backgrounds. This enabled us to teach biology in the context of cultural diversity and globalization, and to evolve new teaching tools. Elements from these new Honors seminars could later be used in the mainstream biology courses. These honor students turned out to be among the best teaching assistants for the regular courses.

I created two new Honors seminars: "Biotechnology in Asia" and "Traditional Chinese Medicine: A Complementary Approach to Modern Western Medicine." In "Biotechnology in Asia," teams of four students were assigned to country teams to examine how biotechnology was used to drive economic development. The countries studied were Japan, China, Singapore, Taiwan, and South Korea. The student teams investigated government policy, research and training, industrial activities, and technology transfer from research laboratories to industry. They learned to write short cables and a final country report plus prepare oral briefings following State Department guidelines. They also made use of a new tool introduced in the new courses involving role plays designed around case studies. An important lesson learned in this course was that, while this group of Asian countries had been successful in applying a new technology, each one had followed a distinct strategy that was consistent with its history and cultural practices. Role playing required the students to think about the actual people creating and using biotechnology in the countries being studied. And, because these case studies were based on actual events, the student teams could compare their performances with the actual outcomes.

"Traditional Chinese Medicine: A Complementary Approach to Modern Western Medicine" examined the philosophical underpinnings, theoretical assumptions, and practical therapeutic approaches of traditional Chinese medicine (TCM) in contrast to modern Western medicine. It was divided into four major modules. The first examined the cultural differences between China and the West and reviewed the development of modern Western medicine, particularly over the past three hundred years. A major conceptual hurdle for American students was to recognize that history and culture mold the development and application of science (medicine in this case). We made use of a lecture on Asian art where visual images of Asian landscapes, black bulls, and prose images of haiku showed how the conventions and values of a culture defined artistic expression. This made it easier to introduce Chinese attitudes towards health and medicine.

The second module reviewed the history of TCM, its conceptual framework, and its practices. The third module looked at the efforts made to modernize TCM using Western science. And the final module looked into the social, legal, and economic hurdles that face TCM in the United States. Under this module, the three main assignments examined three student outcomes:

- Had the student gained a good understanding of the philosophy and principles of TCM and compared them with those of Western medicine?
- Using scientific evidence and clinical proof, could the student apply the perspective of modern Western science to validate the use of TCM in treating a specific medical condition?
- Could the student go beyond scientific and clinical evidence to look at the legal, economic, and social framework in the United States that TCM would have to face in a specific application?

These three Honors seminars were based on a platform that integrated problem solving, case studies, role play, teamwork (where teams are mixed by race, ethnicity, gender, field of study) and peer review. Most of these students were successful in using scientific data to solve complex problems in the context of different cultural situations.

The EAST Project

The creation of novel Honors seminars raised the possibility of disseminating new strategies and tools to other STEM courses at the university. We tried to expand some of our initiatives across our campus and internationally with projects in Thailand and China.

I and a group of STEM faculty at UMCP decided to globalize our curriculum by incorporating East Asian themes into STEM courses. Our first initiative was East Asia Science and Technology, called EAST.

The success of the EAST project very much depended on the principle of faculty-initiated projects and the active participation of faculty and staff. This was achieved by the selection of thirteen colleagues called EAST Fellows: ten faculty from four STEM colleges and three staff members. The EAST Fellows received a small annual stipend in return for which they agreed to attend an annual summer workshop and participate in monthly EAST meetings. Workshops and monthly meetings focused on three distinct areas: concepts and mechanics of creating interdisciplinary and cross-cultural courses, development of Asian cultural modules for integration into existing STEM courses, and effective use of library and technology resources.

Over a period of three years, the EAST program developed, modified and taught East Asian themes within STEM courses. During the period 2002-2004, EAST Fellows modified or created eighteen courses, with a total enrollment of approximately 1,600. Five courses were at the introductory level, eight at mid-level, and five were advanced. Most of the courses included a newly designed module introduced into an existing course. More demanding were the five newly created courses that provided an East Asian perspective to science and engineering: four of them were seminars for Honors students, while the fifth was an interdisciplinary course which fulfilled a general education requirement. There were also two highly unusual types of courses: one for the Young Scholars Program, which prepares high school students for college. The other involved student groups in learning experiences in Asia or Asian students coming to College Park.

One group of UMD students traveled to China and Vietnam for a three-week study abroad experience in January 2006. In addition, there was a noteworthy educational experiment that involved a group of twenty visiting undergraduates from Tokyo's Meiji Gakuin University that participated in a two-week mini-course on Landscape Architecture at UMD. The mini-course involved ten UMD undergraduate Landscape Architecture students learning with Japanese students. Most of the EAST courses have been subject to assessment with the collaboration of the University of Maryland's Center for Teaching Excellence. Student response to the EAST modules and courses has been very positive.

Policy and Educational Reform

In general, I had avoided getting involved in the major national efforts to reform STEM education, since I was uncertain as to how they would change the teaching of individual courses. But when I was asked by Bruce Alberts to join the National Research Council (NRC) to work on science education, I jumped in and got involved.

The first was BIO 2010. Funded by the NIH and the Howard Hughes Medical Institute (HHMI), this initiative examined the undergraduate education of biomedical researchers. Our findings showed a profound need for an interdisciplinary curriculum with an emphasis on current research, teamwork, and laboratory projects. Most universities and colleges did not have such a curriculum, and many of the faculty were incapable or unwilling to carry out the necessary reforms to put one in place. The recommendations of BIO 2010 addressed those deficiencies by proposing a new curriculum that reflected the reality of modern biological research, that it should be interdisciplinary in nature and focused on critical thinking and laboratory research.

In working on BIO 2010, I got to know some of the outstanding teachers in the country and benefited from their ideas on how to integrate math, physics, and chemistry into the teaching of biology. Nevertheless, I saw BIO 2010 as one more well considered report that was unlikely to be implemented on a national scale. When I met with Bruce Alberts to discuss BIO 2010, I was candid in telling him that "it had no legs." However, I had been thinking about my experience in the famous bacterial genetics and bacterial virus courses at the Cold Spring Harbor laboratory. The workshops integrated presentations, discussions, and group projects while the group lived in a summer camp environment. The participants were highly selected and ranged from graduate students to senior investigators, all eager to learn about the new biology. This was a process for educating a new generation of biological scientists. Could we apply the Cold Spring Harbor model to develop new ways to teaching biology?

I shared my thoughts with Millard Sussman, a professor at University of Wisconsin who had taught me at Cold Spring Harbor. He immediately saw the implications of a summer institute for training faculty and gave me his enthusiastic support. When I brought up the idea to Alberts, he instantly understood its implications and put his support behind it. This was the origin of the Summer Institute established under the auspices of the NRC and the HHMI. Its basic concept was to bring together a cadre of teacher-researchers and younger faculty to explore best educational practices. The institute took place at the Madison campus of University of Wisconsin with HHMI financial support and the organizational support of Sussman and his colleagues.

It was generally agreed that the Summer Institute, with its educational STEM research linked to faculty training, was a novel and innovative concept. Its actual implementation revealed a few differences between the principal partners: NRC, HHMI, and UW. The NRC had done the BIO 2010 study and introduced the idea of the Summer Institute. The HHMI had funded both and was a major granting source for universities. The University of Wisconsin provided the venue. The Summer Institute became an HHMI program with HHMI choosing courses, participants, and sites. Its basic role was to develop a curriculum for those students intent on pursuing research careers in medicine. However, it did not address some of the fundamental challenges of introductory courses and the growing diversity of the student pool. Change happens slowly, especially in the field of education.

Faculty Education Abroad

The multiple educational projects at Maryland and related publications attracted international attention. Following a UN conference in Manila, I was invited to give a talk in Bangkok to a group of science faculty. I talked about the concepts of "The Virtual Workplace" and "Journey without Maps," though I was not confident that they would be considered relevant there. It was a happy development, then, that the novel conceptual structures and experiential learning introduced in "The Virtual Workplace" appeared to be universally relevant as an alternative to the traditional model of memorization and recall. I was totally surprised at the interest in diversity. The demographics of science and engineering graduates indicated that most of them came from families in the Bangkok metropolitan area and were predominantly male. "Journey without Maps" addressed the need to expand and diversify the pool of STEM students.

Dr. Yongyuth Yuthavong, director of the National Science and Development Agency, invited me to work as an educational adviser. That summer was spent in a study of the Thai undergraduate science programs and exploring modules that emphasized critical thinking and laboratory research. The latter objective was difficult to achieve in that the NSDA had no direct responsibility for the university curriculum, which was the purview of the Ministry of Education. Finally, Yuthavong and I proposed an Honors program whereby upperclassmen would spend a year doing research at NSDA laboratories.

In most instances, international projects arose from interest in our new approaches to biology courses. In 1980, Taiwan's scientific leadership had placed a high priority on introducing genetic engineering and biotechnology into the country. It had organized a scientific symposium along with eight scientific workshops.

The eight scientific workshops were the critical components of the program. Their purpose was to train local scientists on the techniques and skills for the new technology. In the US, the reagents, radioactive compounds, and enzymes used in biotechnology were just beginning to be commercially available. In Asia and Taiwan, these necessary tools were either unavailable or prohibitively expensive, so our workshop was designed to teach how to produce them in a regular laboratory. The group included laboratory heads, senior faculty, graduate students, and senior technicians. The whole exercise was exhilarating in that, as we were working in a developing country, we had to improvise as we went along. But our students were very good at it, and everyone pitched in as each day lengthened into the night. Sometimes, we would have to duck out in the early evening to attend some official dinner; at other times, some of our students would go out and bring back Chinese takeout dinners, which we would then share at the lab bench. There was an easy camaraderie that was independent of rank and status, something that was not that common in Asia. There were some twenty workshop instructors, most of them originally from Taiwan.

Many years later, we would note that among the new generation of biological scientists were individuals who had taken our workshop all those years ago. It underlined the power of teaching teachers in launching a new technology.

A Chinese Deal

It was a great irony that what was probably my most important educational project came after I had already retired from the University of Maryland. Dr. Dan Mote, president of the University of Maryland at College Park, had made it a priority to establish a partnership with Chinese universities. Dr. Bill Destler, the provost, had asked me to launch an appropriate collaborative venture in science and technology. There were two aspects of this initiative that fascinated me: negotiating a program with the Chinese and creating a long-term partnership that would be of benefit to both the UMD and its Chinese counterpart. I would need to do the due diligence in working out the areas of collaboration and establishing the institutional framework.

To start, I enlisted the assistance of Ray Wu and Bill Tai, who had extensive experience in China and had worked with Gretchen Kalonji, the designer of a collaborative agreement between the University of Washington and Sichuan University. We focused on Sichuan University (SCU), which has a few special characteristics. First, it is located in Chengdu (population 9.65 million, capital of Sichuan Province) in southwest China and had been chosen by the Chinese government to be the principal research university in Western China. Second, Sichuan University, with some 70,000 students, is the result of a merger of three institutions, a comprehensive university, a school of technology, and a school of traditional Chinese medicine, and has strengths in civil engineering, hydrology, ecology and environmental studies, biology, and traditional Chinese medicine. SCU is a major center for the study of minority groups and of the panda. Third, Sichuan University had already been involved in student exchange programs with the University of Washington, Seattle, and Pacific Lutheran University. The personal introductions by Kalonji and her UW colleagues were important in starting our discussions.

I put together a team consisting of the codirectors of the EAST project, along with EAST fellows from the appropriate colleges. We noted a defined need in the Chinese system of higher education, which apparently did not have a way to educate the best and brightest of its students. This was the principal reason for SCU's interest in the University Honors Program at UMD, and led to the immediate support of the Ministry of Education for the creation of an Honors college at SCU. Both universities–in principle–agreed to move towards an exchange for a period of up to one year of twenty-five highly selected STEM undergraduate students. The SCU students would spend their period in the UMD Honors Program, living and studying with American Honor students. The UMD courses would be selected so that the presence of the Chinese students would affect as many US students as possible. The initial cadre of UMD students would be chosen from UMD's Honors Program and would be accepted into SCU's new Honors college. A key aspect of the student experience we envisioned was to have each student work on a research project while attending classes. In the case of the SCU students attending UMD, this would involve a scientific project in the laboratory of a UMD faculty mentor.

The negotiations proceeded at an uneven pace. The Chinese negotiators led by the SCU director for international programs moved speedily and had obtained approval from Beijing. This decision was driven by the Chinese interest in the bilateral agreement between Honors programs on the two campuses. On the US side, the agreement floundered when both Destler at UMD and Kalonji at UW left to take up new positions.

I was disappointed that the agreement did not come to a successful conclusion. I did learn that there were significant differences between the two parties. The Chinese had clear expectations of what they would gain from such a partnership and were willing to take a long view and contribute their resources. Maryland had a much shorter time horizon with the expectation of financial gains.

It was an object lesson on the complexities of negotiating a multi-dimensional agreement with the Chinese. On the Chinese side, it was critical to identify the right organization and its needs. On the US side, the situation was more complex in terms of our priorities, and it was not unusual that any agreement was seen as a source of profits for the US side requiring the support of multiple academic units.

Reflections of a Teacher

Some who teach delude themselves into believing that what they teach their students will last a lifetime. My hope, however, is that I will motivate them to learn for themselves. I want to see my students raising questions and then, through a process of discovery, dig for and find a solution. This is very different from having someone else "teach" you the answer. When my students learn for themselves and from their peers and mentors, they gain more than an answer to their original questions. They learn to think, to delve, to solve bigger and more far reaching problems.

My teaching experience was unusual in that it was connected with research, public policy, and international collaboration. I could not conceive of courses of study that did not incorporate those elements into contemporary science courses. I was able to do this in different ways, including the design and implementation of new biology courses, work toward institutional change at the university level, reform at the national level, and international collaboration.

The latter two were difficult, even intractable. Curriculum change requires serious money, training, and time. External grants may fund "proof of concept" experimental courses, but universities have to sustain these courses. Equally important, new curricula require not just faculty training but a fundamental change in faculty values, where excellent teaching is often neither recognized nor rewarded.

The responsibilities among faculty include research, service, teaching. The first two are easy to quantify in terms of funding (grants, contracts), while the rewards of teaching have, traditionally, been more "spiritual." In research, there are also drivers that go beyond financial reward. If you are a gifted scientist, you may take a high risk pursuing long shot projects, but you may earn the respect of your peers for your imagination and sense of adventure. This is not true for teaching, which requires not only imagination and effort but personal involvement with your students. Your students may love you, but the system does not reward you for your efforts and commitment. To improve teaching, we must change the value systems in schools, universities, and the government departments whose decisions have tremendous impact on every teacher and student in the country.

National reform is on the agenda of many educational organizations. While there are three government agencies that deal with education, the United States Department of Education, the National Science Foundation, and the National Institutes of Health, none of them has a leading role in STEM education. The same is true of most private foundations with the possible exception of the Howard Hughes Medical Institute in the area of education for medical research. The end result is that curriculum change in STEM education remains slow and sporadic.

The international projects depended on the objectives and cost sharing by the participants. In those projects which were commissioned by foreign governments (e.g., Taiwan's biotechnology workshops, Thailand's assessment of STEM education), the objectives were defined and funded by the foreign government, and the results were most satisfactory. The Sichuan-Maryland project was the most ambitious and complex one, but also the most frustrating in the financial and academic political issues on the US side that led to an incomplete outcome.

I have been fortunate to have been able to work at multiple levels in STEM education, both in the US and abroad. My greatest satisfaction has been working in real courses with real students and collaborating with colleagues that brought the same passion to their work. Teaching is a big job. Two events illustrate the plusses and minuses.

At a NRC meeting, I had lunch with a colleague and member of the National Academy of Sciences who was interested in my educational projects. After I had summarized them, he asked, "How did the university reward you for all of that work? Let me guess, some university awards and possibly one or two cash prizes, for a few thousand dollars?"

"Yes," I responded. "Three or four awards. The biggest cash award was $3,000."

"And you probably get more on a daily rate for consulting to a pharmaceutical company?"

Of course he was right, but there is much that money cannot buy.

I had finished teaching my senior level "Microbial Physiology" course when one of my students walked up to me. She was one of the best students but had always been very reticent.

"I just wanted to thank you for teaching this class," she said quietly. "You made me feel like I was your junior partner on a scientific project. You treated me as an equal capable of meeting the challenges of a scientific career today."

In the end, that was what teaching was all about: not for money, not for power, not for recognition, but for the hope that at some point, over the years of teaching, you have made a difference in your students.

THOUGHTS ON THE BEAUTIFUL COUNTRY
From China to the West and Back Again

I have lived in exciting times. I was born in Paris, grew up in Havana, and spent much of my life in America and Europe. My experience of the world was further shaped by two of the great revolutions of the 20th Century: China and Cuba as well as by revolutions in science, technology, and education. My identity was shaped by a combination of Chinese and Cuban cultures blended into the larger American one with a strong European influence.

My father saw the loss of his homeland and his diplomatic career. Thus, his advice to me was to choose a different career, a safer one in science, and a new homeland. Science was to be my future and America my sanctuary. I dove into chemistry, physics, molecular biology. I learned about the genetics and physiology of bacteria and their viruses, and the techniques for working on DNA and its complex interactions. I learned to appreciate the elegant design of experiments and the writing of scientific manuscripts. I also learned other important aspects of science: to transmit the new knowledge to young students and to apply science and rationality to policy issues. Still, although my path diverged radically from my father's, the value he placed on understanding the people and cultures of the world and interacting meaningfully with them was not lost on me. I like to think I continued that family tradition all the way through. I also never let go of China.

China: The Long March to the Future

The history of modern China is frequently seen as the period from the establishment of the People's Republic of China in 1949 to the present day. It is more accurate to think of China in the context of more than three thousand years of history and the many recurring themes that are deeply embedded in its culture:

- China as the center of the world
- Virtuous Emperor: the emperor has absolute power as long as he fulfills the needs of his people
- Mandate of Heaven: the power of the emperor is revoked when he no longer fulfills his duty to his people and a new emperor rises from the masses
- Family as a social organizing principle
- Pragmatism is seen as a fundamental value. This is often expressed in the form of a meritocracy.

Relatively little attention has been paid to the period of Republican China when the Nationalists led by Chiang Kai Shek tried to unify and modernize China as they struggled against the Communists and tried to fight off the invading Japanese. The Communists learned certain bitter lessons from their victory:

China's need for self-sufficiency, freedom from foreign allies, and the organization of its peasant masses around Mao's Marxist ideology. The radical efforts of the Great Leap Forward and the Cultural Revolution were unsuccessful in bringing forth China's modernization and economic development.

Starting in the 1990's, China has evolved into the Grand Compromise that combines the liberalization of the economy with the political monopoly by the Communist Party. Most Chinese would agree that China today is in a transition state and there is no clear consensus on what a modern Chinese nation will look like nor what role democracy may play in it.

There is a broader China world that encompasses all of the ethnic Chinese that do not live under the direct rule of the People's Republic. They total some 50 million that live in special autonomous regions of the PRC such as Macau and Hong Kong or in independent states such as Taiwan and Singapore. They comprise minorities living in countries such as Malaysia, Indonesia, Thailand. The role of these "outlanders" is important and opaque, but it is certain that they are the largest investors in the PRC. They are important sources of technology and provide important models for China's political and economic development.

Not too long ago, I was the host at a dinner in Washington. The nine guests were Chinese originating from different parts of the Chinese world, and all of them were scientists and technocrats. Everyone agreed that today's China is a country in evolution, and when it came to its future, it seemed to be summarized in one word: Singapore. Singapore is modern, wealthy, international, technologically and economically advanced. Its values are Chinese, and it practices a form of single party, controlled democracy where stability and order are preeminent. The basic argument is that culture and history shape destiny. However, today's Greater China provides a far more complex picture with five jurisdictions ruled by Chinese majorities (China, Taiwan, Hong Kong, Macau, Singapore). And while they all share common values, language, and history, they have evolved into distinct systems ranging from a hybrid form of Communist capitalism to a surprisingly open form of free market democracy in Taiwan. We could not but speculate on how modern China could adopt one of the existing models, though the struggle for the future of Hong Kong suggests that this might be a long and arduous challenge.

Journey Without Maps

I have looked upon myself as an American both by education and upbringing. Though my early years had been in Cuba, my undergraduate and graduate education had been in the U.S. as had been most of my professional life. But deep down, I have a deep legacy rooted in China.

Recently, I decided to teach an adult course on "China: The Long March to the Future," which started me thinking of the many ways in which I had been exposed to the Chinese world. As luck would have it, I traveled to China a number of times over a period of thirty years as 1.3 billion people there went through changes that were unprecedented in human history. The purposes for these trips were very different. I was, of course, able to visit family. I also conducted technology and biotech assessments in China and Hong Kong and wrote articles and reviews on Chinese biotechnology for the U.S. journal *Genetic Engineering News*. My wife, Yuan, and I traveled there to develop a project using Traditional Chinese Medicine in modern prescription drugs. And, in my role as educational administrator, I worked in China to design a collaborative project between U.S. and Chinese universities.

Each trip was a distinct experience not only because of the rapid changes going on there, but also because I was meeting and working with such a variety of groups and people (government officials, business executives, scientists, academics) that differed in jobs, age, and experience.

A reader of this book is likely to fall into one of two major categories. Some of you will recognize similar experiences in your own life: the sense of discovery, the exotic nature of foreign lands and disparate cultures. This kind of existence is strangely addictive and conducive to a search for new experiences. For others, this type of life is fraught with risk and uncertainty and should be best avoided. As the stage characters Rosencrantz and Guildenstern described it, life was made up of choices that were affected by a changing world and individuals with varying interests. My choices were impacted by a diversity of cultures: Hispanic, Chinese, European, America, and about science in multiple forms, the search for new knowledge, teaching it to a new generation, applying it in health and medicine, and examining its impact on society. America provided a platform that gave me, a foreigner, the freedom to express my ideas and pursue new opportunities. And it's been a fantastic ride.

Acknowledgements

This book has two principal components: its writing and the sum total of the diverse activities which are described in it. The author was fortunate of having had Matthew Meselson and Werner Arber as mentors in his formative years. Each in his way combined a lucid and elegant approach to science with teaching excellence, participation in government policy, and international cooperation.

A number of individuals have helped with this book: John Sterling, Les Glick, David Myers, Ben Martynoga, Ying-Ying Yuan, and Peg Corl. In the years dedicated to diplomacy and technology assessment, the following provided valuable assistance and support: Al Hellman, Michael Kelley, Michael Mercurio, George Liu, Michael Hsu, Michael Ma, Luis Morera, and Patricia Tsien. Intense efforts at novel teaching techniques were shared with Spencer Benson, Maynard Mack, Ann Smith, and James Greenberg. Space makes it impossible to include the names of the many who have helped me in my endeavors particularly in Europe, Asia, and the Americas. For that I apologize.
Life is not only work. My quality of life has been sustained and enhanced by my sister, Rosie Kim, and her husband, Sung-Hou Kim, and my daughter, Nikki Yuan. I am grateful that my wife, Yuan Lin, has shared life's adventures in so many of these times and places, worked with me on this book, and contributed the original design for this book cover.

About the Author

Robert Yuan, PhD, is a scientist, diplomat, and educator. He did research in molecular biology at Harvard University, Edinburgh University, University of Basel, and the National Cancer Institute. As a foreign service officer, he carried out two major studies on technology competitiveness in Western Europe and Asia and was Asian editor for *Genetic Engineering News*. As a professor at the University of Maryland, Yuan developed new biology courses that introduced themes of globalization and diversity for which he received several university awards for teaching excellence. He also served on the Board of Biology of the U.S. National Research Council.

Living along the Chesapeake Bay, Yuan teaches adult education courses on China and writes articles on Asia.

Made in the USA
Middletown, DE
09 August 2023